THE ROMAN DRAWINGS

OF THE XVII & XVIII CENTURIES

IN THE COLLECTION OF

HER MAJESTY THE QUEEN

AT WINDSOR CASTLE

BY

ANTHONY BLUNT

AND

HEREWARD LESTER COOKE

LONDON

THE PHAIDON PRESS LTD

*The reproductions in this volume are from a new set
of photographs taken by John R. Freeman*

MADE IN GREAT BRITAIN
PRINTED BY GEO. GIBBONS LTD · LEICESTER
BOUND BY A. W. BAIN & CO. LTD · LONDON

CONTENTS

PREFACE

THE preparation of this volume of the Catalogue has been spread over a long period. Work was begun towards the end of the war, when it was proposed that the volume should be the result of collaboration between Professor Rudolf Wittkower and myself. At that time Professor Wittkower made a large number of attributions, many of which have been confirmed by further research and are incorporated in this volume, and the Editors wish to express their gratitude to him for his valuable contribution to the catalogue. This contribution was not limited to these preliminary attributions, since the entries on Bernini have been for the greater part drawn from his monumental work on that master's drawings. In certain cases I have ventured to differ from the opinions recorded in Professor Wittkower's catalogue raisonné, but in many of these cases he has expressed his agreement with the deviations from his first text.

For various reasons work on the volume had to be set aside by both the original authors, and when the time came to take it up again, Professor Wittkower had been appointed to a post at Columbia University and was therefore unable to continue the work. His place was taken by Mr. Hereward Lester Cooke of the National Gallery of Art, Washington, whose knowledge of other collections of Seicento drawings has proved of the greatest value. Mr. Cooke was given grants by the National Gallery of Art in 1957 and 1959 to work on this project.

The shares of the two collaborators should be clearly defined. The large groups of drawings by Maratta, Sacchi, Bernini, and Schor were entirely my responsibility, but the remaining entries are the result of collaboration. In fairness it should however be added that, being the Editor on the spot, I have had to make a number of minor last-minute additions and alterations without always consulting my colleague.

Many scholars have generously supplied information on individual sections or drawings: Mr. Francis Dowley on Maratta; Dr. Walter Vitzthum on Pietro da Cortona; Mr. Anthony Clark on Batoni; Mr. Cornelius Vermeule on drawings after the Antique, and Dr. Karl Noehles on an architectural drawing by Pietro da Cortona. In addition Professor E. K. Waterhouse put at my disposal his photographs of Roman Seicento painting and made a number of extremely valuable suggestions. Mr. Keith Roberts undertook the job of tracing related material in the British Museum and the Witt Library.

Without the continuous help of Miss Elsa Scheerer the catalogue would probably never have reached completion, and, if it had done so, it would have contained many more inaccuracies and inconsistencies.

I wish once more to thank all those concerned with the Royal Library for their cooperation and help. Sir Owen Morshead was Librarian during the greater part of the gestation period of this catalogue and gave, as always, unstinted encouragement. His successor, Mr. Robert Mackworth-Young, has greatly helped in the last stages, and Miss Scott-Elliot has contributed to this volume even more than to previous ones by supplying accurate descriptions of a large number of drawings for the catalogue, as well as checking those innumerable details which arise in a work of this kind. A.F.B.

INTRODUCTION

THERE are five major collections of Roman Seicento drawings in the world: in the Louvre, in the Gabinetto Nazionale delle Stampe, Rome, in the Kunstmuseum at Düsseldorf, in the Albertina in Vienna, and in the Royal Library at Windsor. Of all these the last is, with the possible exception of the Louvre, the richest and the most representative.

The Roman drawings at Windsor were almost all in the Royal Collection in the reign of George III and are included in the Inventory drawn up at this time. Apart from roughly half the Carracci drawings, which came via Consul Smith from the Bonfiglioli collection in Bologna, they seem with very few exceptions to have come from the collection of Cardinal Giovanni Francesco Albani, which was bought for the King by James Adam in 1762. The Cardinal had inherited this collection from his uncle, Clement XI, at the death of the latter in 1721. The core of it was formed by the drawings bought by the Pope from Maratta in 1703, which included the Domenichinos, probably the Andrea Sacchis and, one may imagine, a large part of the seventeenth-century drawings by Roman artists. Additions were no doubt made to this great nucleus after it had passed into the possession of George III, since it is known that his librarian, Richard Dalton, made frequent journeys to Italy to buy paintings and drawings; but unfortunately these transactions are imperfectly documented.

Some sections of the Roman drawings at Windsor have already been covered in previous parts of this catalogue, and the present volume must be considered as belonging to a sort of trilogy, the other two parts being Professor Wittkower's catalogue of the Carracci drawings and Mr. Pope-Hennessy's volume on Domenichino. In effect, therefore, the first chapter of the history of Roman drawing in the seventeenth century has already been told, and the achievement of the first generation of artists dealt with in these two volumes. For this reason the present catalogue opens, generally speaking, with the second generation: Andrea Sacchi, continuing the classical tradition, and Lanfranco, Bernini and Pietro da Cortona creating the full baroque. Again the picture has to be completed from another group of drawings, because Nicolas Poussin, whose drawings have been dealt with under the French School, played a vital part on the side of classicism in this phase.

There are, however, included in the present volume certain drawings which date from the first decades of the century and which deserve particular mention, especially two studies of heads (Pls. 2 and 3). The technique is conventional and could be paralleled in many draughtsmen of the period both in Rome and in Bologna; but the observation of wrinkled details suggests an artist who knew the work of Caravaggio and his followers, and the audacious exploitation of the long protruding eyebrows, and the nose disappearing in the *profil perdu* view are unthinkable in Bolognese art and would be hard to parallel in Rome. The closest analogy is to be found in the paintings of Orazio Gentileschi, but as no drawings by him are known it would be reckless to attribute this remarkable pair to him.

The opposing groups in the battle of classicism and baroque about the middle of the century are brilliantly represented at Windsor. The drawings by Sacchi, more than 130 in number, form one of the two most important groups of the kind in existence (the other being at Düsseldorf) and show the artist's talent—one could not say genius—to the best advantage. In type they range from rough pen sketches, incorporating the first idea of a composition, to carefully worked out studies for each detail of a single composition, as in the case of the *Destruction of the pagan idols* (Fig. 72), or the studies for an unexecuted ceiling design (Pls. 26, 27). These two groups date from the last years of the artist's life, but his earlier style is also well represented, as, for instance, by the study of *St. Gregory* of 1625. The series also contains drawings quite outside his normal range, such as the *Dance in Casa Falconieri* (Fig. 76), the study for an altar (Fig. 75)—one of the very few architectural drawings which can be attributed to him with any degree of probability—or the water-colour designs for Barberini tapestries (Fig. 77).

More positive in his classicism and more personal in his style is Sassoferrato, whose sixty drawings at Windsor constitute practically his entire surviving output in this medium. The particular qualities of this artist come out in more attractive form in his drawings than in his paintings, in which the sentiment is somewhat sweet and the handling too smooth for twentieth-century taste. The greater part of the drawings at Windsor consists of finished studies for religious compositions, many of which can be identified; but a less familiar aspect of his art is revealed by the portrait drawings (Pls. 34, 35). One of these (Pl. 35) is for a known painting, and others, already squared, were evidently used for canvases now untraceable; but the series also contains a group of four heads (cf. Pls. 38, 39) larger in scale, and executed in coloured chalks, which seem, like contemporary French drawings by the Dumonstier family, to be intended as complete works in themselves. Such drawings are extremely rare in Italian art of the seventeenth century. Leoni's portraits provide a partial parallel, but are much smaller in scale.

To these two important groups of works by the classical artists of the second generation must be added a few drawings by others attached to the same party. Pietro Testa, the imitator of Poussin and the friend of Cassiano dal Pozzo, appears with a few small sketches and an allegory on the evils of wealth, accompanied by a long explanatory letter; and to that ill-defined and elusive figure, Pier Francesco Mola, can be assigned some rapid and brilliant sketches drawn in his characteristic style in strokes of unusual flexibility and variety made with a soft reed pen (Pls. 40–42).

Against these relatively academic artists we may set the creators of the Roman baroque. The oldest of these, Giovanni Lanfranco, makes a rather poor figure in his drawings, which he evidently regarded as mere tools to be used in the execution of paintings and never as finished works of art. Those in pen and wash (Fig. 35) have a certain dramatic vitality but the greater part consist of black chalk studies of single figures used in one or other of Lanfranco's fresco cycles. Their style is free and often seems almost careless, and the fact that they are faintly drawn on blue-grey or green-grey paper and sometimes rubbed means that they make little impression in reproduction. A few of them (Pls. 4, 5) date from the artist's early phase and show him still working in the manner of his master, Annibale Carracci, but most of the Windsor series are connected with his later works in Naples; in fact they probably include the remains of a single sketchbook dating from that period. One curious feature of the figure studies is that often they do not correspond exactly with any one fresco but come close to two or more. Several, for instance, might equally well be claimed as preparatory sketches for the *Apostles* in SS. Apostoli or for those in S. Martino, but they do not quite correspond to either. In fact it looks as though Lanfranco kept a stock of drawings, which he drew on as needed and varied in each particular case. His methods will, however, not be fully understood till the 600 drawings in the museum of Capodimonte at Naples have been thoroughly examined.

As a draughtsman Lanfranco is entirely overshadowed by Bernini, the greatest figure in Roman baroque drawing. The Royal Library does not have the monopoly in Bernini that it has in some other artists, such as Domenichino or Sassoferrato, but the series shows to the full his achievement as a draughtsman. The most spectacular performances are the black chalk designs for fountains (Pls. 13, 14), in which the freedom and richness of the black chalk is the perfect vehicle for expressing the movement of the whole design. A precise pen line is used for the more precious first scheme for the Fontana del Moro on the Piazza Navona (Pl. 11). New light is thrown on the general project for this square by an un-published drawing, unfortunately damaged, which may be for a Fountain of Neptune to balance the Fontana del Moro at the other end of the Piazza. The series includes many studies for monuments and altars in Rome and elsewhere, including an unpublished design for the new panel and inscription to be erected over the Porta Santa at St. Peter's in the Holy Year of 1650. Bernini's achievement as a portrait draughtsman is brilliantly displayed at Windsor in examples beginning with that of a boy (Pl. 8), often said to be a self-portrait, and ending with the grave depiction of the artist in his later years, probably dating from about the time of his disastrous visit to Paris in 1665 (Pl. 9).

The volumes made up in the eighteenth century and devoted to the work of Bernini inevitably contained many drawings by pupils and imitators. One group of these (Pls. 45, 46 and Figs. 100, 101) can be associated with his most talented assistant in the field of decor-ative art, Giovanni Paolo Schor, also known as Giovanni Paolo Tedesco, who was the leading member of a family of Tyrolese artists who settled in Rome. When Bernini was in Paris, he mentioned him as an artist who would have been very useful to Louis XIV if he could have been persuaded to come to Paris. In his diary of the visit[1] Chantelou records that Bernini spoke of him as a man 'ayant un fond de dessin et d'invention inépuisable et propre a tout', and he added: 'Veut-on un carosse? il en fait le dessin; une chaise? un dessin; de l'argenterie? un dessin, et généralement de tout'. Figs. 100, 101 give a clear idea of the kind of sketch to which Bernini was referring, thrown off in a moment; but equal virtuosity appears in the more finished drawings, such as the two for coaches (Pls. 45, 46). One design, for a fantastic clock (p. 12), foreshadows ideas normally associated with the picturesque phase of the eighteenth century. Schor seems to have designed several works in this mood. The fountains in the Palazzo Borghese are his, and the Guides to Rome describe a fantastic room in the principal apartment of the Palazzo Altieri, which went even further in this direction. It consists, they say, of 'an artificial cave, composed of mountains and rocks. Inside is a bed made of tree-trunks, a table, a fountain, stools to sit on, a *prie-dieu* for paying devotions to a wax figure and a painting of St. Mary Magdalen, the whole designed by Giovanni Paolo Schor Tedesco. The idea is very beautiful, and is executed with much

[1] Chantelou, *Journal du Voyage du Cavalier Bernin en France*, Paris, 1885, pp. 222–23. Cf. also pp. 213, 231.

magnificence in the form of a hermitage'.[2] No drawing for this scheme is known, but a finished design (p. 193), apparently for a tapestry, with the Altieri arms is presumably connected with Schor's decoration of the Palace.

The drawings of Pietro da Cortona do not have either the imaginative force or the technical virtuosity of Bernini's works in this medium, but the finest of them, such as *Alexander besieging Pera* (Pl. 17), apparently made for an engraving, are as mature and complete as his best frescoes. More personal are the very late sketches, such as the *Death of Turnus* for the Pamphili Gallery (Pl. 21), which has a fiery intensity lacking in the earlier and more accomplished drawings.

In his architectural designs, considered as drawings, Pietro da Cortona may be said to have excelled even Bernini and to have been excelled only by Borromini. Bernini's drawings for architectural schemes are often mere scribbles, made as notes of a general idea with no thought of their aesthetic quality, and, when more finished, their emphasis is principally on the sculptural parts of the scheme. Although Cortona was a painter his drawings, for instance the design for his tomb (Fig. 59) or for the *Quarantore* at San Lorenzo in Damaso (Fig. 58), show a fine and clear grasp of architectural form as well as for the decorative details, and the artist employs a peculiarly firm and wiry line to express these features.

As the author of the eighteenth-century inventory says: 'The Drawings of Pietro da Cortona and Ciro Ferri are so similar that they are seldom distinguish'd'. In particular Ferri excelled in a kind of finished black chalk drawing based on Cortona's technique but more academic in feeling. *Moses striking the Rock* (Pl. 43) is an exceptionally large and elaborate example of Ferri's work in this style, which can fortunately be attributed to him with certainty on the basis of an engraving. The artist appears in a freer and more personal mood in the big drawing, made up of two sheets, for a fresco illustrating the story of Perseus (Figs. 19, 20). This drawing also shows how closely he followed his master in his architectural forms.

The other immediate followers of Pietro da Cortona do not merit detailed discussion. The drawings of Romanelli reveal a weakness which might be suspected from his paintings. Of the two Courtois brothers, Jacques and Guillaume, known as Giacomo and Guglielmo Cortese or Borgognone, the latter is no morethan a direct continuer of his master's manner, but Giacomo's more individual interests appear in his drawings of battle scenes, which probably include the huge drawing of the *Victory of Alexander over Porus* (Fig. 63), based no doubt on a design by Cortona but with the stamp of the Burgundian in the details of execution and in the drawing of the horses, in which he was a specialist.

The true baroque tradition was carried on till the end of the seventeenth century by a small group of artists of whom one, the Genoese Giovanni Battista Gaulli, usually called Baciccio, is well represented at Windsor. Generally speaking, however, the taste of those who formed this collection inclined towards a more classical form of art, as it was manifested in the person of Carlo Maratta, the most important Roman painter of the later seventeenth century and in his later years the most celebrated artist in Europe. Maratta was a prolific draughtsman, and the drawings at Windsor—more than 270 in number—are only a part of his production (there are more than a thousand drawings from his hand or his studio at Düsseldorf). They are of particular importance in that they come from the

2 Pinarola, *L'Antichità di Roma*, 1713, ii, p. 150.

Albani Collection and were probably bought by Clement XI either from the artist or from his heirs.

If Maratta had drawn less, he would probably have been admired more. There are many drawings by him which, taken individually, show great vigour as well as competence, and it is only when we see so many more, exactly similar, that doubts are aroused and we begin to feel that it came almost too easily to the artist and that he could turn out these productions with too little effort. His range, however, was immense. He was a master of the academic drawing of the nude (Pl. 59), or of the draped figure (Pl. 58); he was inventive in the composition of large religious subjects (Pls. 52–55); he could be rugged and vigorous with the pen (Pl. 54), or careful and finished in red chalk (Pl. 57). This universal adaptability played a great part in his success, as did a similar gift for his French contemporary Charles Le Brun. The parallel might be pushed further, for both of them evolved a blend of classicism with elements of the baroque which was palatable to the public in their own country and was also of a kind that could be exported. Maratta and Carlo Fontana in Rome, and Le Brun and J. H. Mansart in France may be said to have created the international baroque style in painting and architecture which laid the foundation for a great part of European art in the eighteenth century.

Maratta's immediate followers are well represented at Windsor, Pietro de Pietri by an important series of drawings, several of them connected with paintings, and Giuseppe Passeri by many specimens in his characteristic style of pen and wash over strong underdrawing in red chalk[3]; and the story is carried on to the middle of the eighteenth century by groups of works by Stefano Pozzo, Agostino Masucci and Sebastiano Conca, and still later by the works attributed to Batoni. Here we are in *terra incognita* as far as connoisseurship of drawings is concerned, though the work being done by younger scholars, particularly in America, will soon change this situation. In the meantime the drawings at Windsor can supply a few attributions and a few pointers of a more general kind.

Taken as a whole the later Roman drawings in the Royal Library form one of the most complete and representative groups in the whole collection. If we compare it for instance with the series of later Venetian drawings, the contrast is striking. The latter contains—in round numbers—350 drawings by Sebastiano and Marco Ricci (excluding the caricatures), 150 by Antonio Visentini, 140 by Canaletto, one by Domenico Tiepolo, none by his father, and none by any member of the Guardi family. In the case of Rome all the major artists of the seventeenth century are represented by fine, in some cases unparalleled, groups of drawings; and there is hardly even a minor painter who does not figure in the collection, usually with drawings which can be related to known works.[4]

The Windsor series therefore provides an unusually good basis for the study of both the greater and the lesser draughtsmen of the Roman Seicento. For this reason the Editors have been at particular pains to identify and, as far as possible, reproduce drawings related to known works and so to provide firm starting points for gaining a knowledge of draughtsmen whose style is in many cases hardly determined. To this hard core of material they have

---

[3] There are also drawings by Daniel Seiter, but these will be catalogued in the section dealing with the German School.

[4] The only important figures not so represented are the decorative artists Andrea Pozzo, Giovanni Coli and Filippo Gherardi, but drawings by the last two are scarcely known.

added, with the qualification 'attributed to', a number of drawings which appear to them to be connected with the artist in question. In some cases these attributions are based on tradition or old inscriptions, but in others they are made purely on stylistic grounds. In this way they hope to have achieved a preliminary sorting of the large mass of anonymous drawings, though this classification will no doubt be subject to much revision by others working in the field. Many drawings had to be left in the anonymous category, as will be seen from the last section of the catalogue. The most interesting of these unidentified drawings have been included in small reproductions, in the hope that other students of the subject may be able to suggest identifications.

A.F.B.

SCHOR: DESIGN FOR A CLOCK (Cat. No. 946).

EXTRACTS FROM INVENTORY "A"

(p. 104)

GIOVANBATISTA SALVI detto il SASSO FERRATO
(= Inv. Nos. 6046–6112)

67. Study's for Various Pictures of Madonnas &c.ᵃ mostly copied from Raphael, Guido & others (as He was not fertile in Invention) with several Portraits drawn from the Life.

(p. 106)   ANDREA SACCHI
Tom. I (= Inv. Nos. 4854–4909)

2. Various figures in two Compartments.

1. The Sketch of the death of St. Ann, painted in the Church of St. Carlo Cattinaro at Rome, and engrav'd by Jacomo Freij.

1. A Sketch of the St. Gregory, painted at St. Peters, Rome.

1. A neat Copy of his Picture of Ham deriding his Father Noah.

5. Various Study's, the first Christ going to be Crucified.

2. A Sketch of a Ball. And a Drawings of Caricaturas.

7. Study's of Boys & Men with Academical figures as Ornaments.

5. Heads. A Figure in an Angle. And a Sketch.

6. Three Heads. Three Figures, two with Drapery's.

25. Two of Heads, and Twenty three Academical figures.

55.

Tom. II (The first part = Inv. Nos. 4921–4972; the drawings in the second part distributed under their artists' names).

52. Study's for various Compositions and Academical Figures.

ACCADEMIE DI DIVERSI AUTORI

14. Of Andrea Sacchi. And Pietro da Cortona.

4. Benedetto Luti, and Angelo Canini.

5. Bernini.

6. Carlo Maratti.

10. Two Camasei. One Solimene, One Mola, One Annibale Carracci, One Ludovico Carracci, One Rubens, One Copy, Two Carlo Maratti.

40.

(p. 107)   CARLO MARATTI
Tom. I (= Inv. Nos. 4091–4141)

2. Two designs for Monuments, Engrav'd by F. Bartolozzi.

2. Hagar & Ishmael. V:M: appearing to Saints.

2. Tobias with the Angel & family. A Sketch with a Pen for an Altar piece at the Madonna del Popolo, varied from this in the painting.

4. The first a Sketch for an Altar piece, & three other Study's.

5. A Sketch for the Picture of the V:M: St. Roch & St. Francis (with the long Neck) at Monte Santo near the Porta del Popolo. St. Francis. A Jael having slain Sisera. A Woman half figure. A Large Virgin & Child.
NB: The three first are Engrav'd by Various.

14. Study's of Heads.

21. A Study of Lucretia, and two others, one a Christ, three Study's also for one of the four Evangelists. Painted in the Angles of a Cupola at St. Peters. Thirteen various Study's and Two Academical Figures.

50.

Tom. II (= Inv. Nos. 4142–4175)

2. The Angel with Tobias, & the Spouse with her Attendants. The Emblem of Sculpture. These are Engrav'd by F. Bartolozzi.

9. V:M: St. Francis and Angels, a Sketch for an Altar piece. Another Legend of an Angel, Saints, &c. Christ working of Miracles. St. Margaret demolishing the Dragon. A Picture of the V: Mary supported by Angels. St. Filippo Neri. V:M: St. Francis & St. Roch. St. Luke painting the V: Marys pictures. A Pietà or V:M: and the Dead Christ.

5. A Calk of a Drawing of a Pietà. V:M: & a young Jesuit Saint. St. Stanislaus. A Sketch of a Monument on the other side. Saints in Paradise, with Study's of Heads on the back of the Drawing. Apollo or the Chariot of the Sun, unknown.

8. Study's of Heads.

9. V:M: Child & St. John. St. Matthew. St. James. Six various Study's. Two Academical amongst them.

33.

(p. 108)   Tom. III (= Inv. Nos. 4176–4228)

11. The Arts rewarded out of a Cornucopia. A Sketch of the descent of the Holy Ghost. The presentation to the Temple. The four Evangelists. St. Francis, engraved by R. Van Audanaerd. King David. Isaiah & two more Prophets, in Angles under a Cupola. An Angel sitting on the Globe.

20. Study's for various Pictures of Genii, and the remainder Ornaments.

22. Of Heads, Madonnas. Christ. St. John. Angels, and two or three from Raphael. And a Portrait of a Young Man with long curling Hair.

___
53.

Tom. IV (= Inv. Nos. 4229–4280)

42. Contains Forty two Drawings in Red Chalk, after the Paintings of Raphael in the Vatican at Rome.

10. The Drawings after the Painting of Domenichino, of the Scourging of St. Andrew, in the Church of St. Gregorio at Rome, and etch'd by Carlo Maratti. Five Drawings after Correggio. Three Study's of his own and one from Michael Angelo.

___
52.

(p. 109)   Tom. V (= Inv. Nos. 4281–4333)

14. After the History of the Bible, design'd by Raphael & Painted by himself & Scholars, In the Loggia of the Vatican at Rome.

17. The miraculous draught of Fishes. The Conversion of St. Paul. Ananias Struck dead. Four Study's from the Adoration of the Kings & one from the Sacrafice. St. Paul preaching at Athens, and Christ delivering the Keys to St. Peter. Three more figures from the Adoration. Two from the Presentation at the Temple. The greatest part of their going to Sacrafice to Paul & Barnabas, with the Study of St. Paul.

   NB.—All these from the Tapestry's at Rome work'd from the designs of Raphael of which the seven famous Cartoons now in Queens Pallace are the only remaining ones.

11. The Galatea after Raphael, in the little Farnese Pallace. The Head of Neptune and a Zephyr in the Council of the Gods, at the same Pallace where the Loves of Cupid & Psyche are painted. Two Madonna's. a Janus & Saturn. A Charity. Faith & Hope in rounds. A V:M: & Child sitting on a Throne. Almost all this Volume are Study's from Raphael.

___
42.

Tom. VI (= Inv. Nos. 4345–4395)

4. Faith Triumphant on a piece of Architecture. David with the Head of Goliah. St. Francis raising the Dead. Study for the rape of the Sabines.

9. An Altarpiece, Three Women Saints above & three River Gods under. Asumption of the V:M: A Dead Christ with the Marys St. John &c, Erminia with Shepherds. Hagar & Ishmael. A Magdalen. A Sybil. St. Jerome. and St. Francis.

5. Venus Cupid and Vulcan. Holy Family. Flight into Egypt. Holy Family. Saints an Altarpiece.

8. Portrait of a Country Girl. Study for a Magdalen. A large Head. Portrait of a Friar. Academical Study.

A Study of two Figures for the Drapery. Two old Heads.

6. Study's from Antique Basso Relievo's.

15. From the Ancient Statues.

4. Lyons head's and Sphynx.

___
51.

(p. 110) PASSARI, PIETRO DE PETRIS &c:
Tom. I (= Inv. Nos. 01231, 0261–0278, 5644–5665)

20. Mostly Historical, Sacred and Profane, The first Drawing is the Design for a large Altar Piece, of St. Benedict receiving a young Prince in his Convent, which is Engrav'd.

   NB – None of his Drawings are finished, but great Spirit and a flow of Invention in all his Works.

21. Ditto of Pietro de Petris. And five of the School of Carlo Maratti.

___
41.

Tom. II (= Inv. Nos. 4396–4436, 097)

10. Heads in red & Black Chalk, with Drawings on the back of two by Pietro de Petris,

33. Drawings of Pietro de Petris. Massuci and other Scholars of Carlo Maratti, excepting one Caricatura by Ghezzi.

___
43.

(p. 111)   PIETRO BERETINO DA CORTONA
Tom. I (= Inv. Nos. 4508–4547)

7. The fall of the Giants. Prophets, in the Angle of a Cupola. The Conversion of St. Paul. Moses breaking the Tables on seeing the Idolatry of the Israelites. Mutius Scaevola. Noah his family and all the Animals entering the Ark. Tullia the Wife of Tarquin driving her Chariot over her Father, Servius Tullius.

17. Triumph of Bacchus. V:M: in Glory. a General shewn the Appearance of the V:M: in the Sky. Saints in Glory, one one side, & four Figures descending in a Cloud on the other side. A: Guardian Angel. A Battle. Solomon and the Queen of Sheba. The Sacrafice of Iphigenia. The Combatt of Æneas and Turnus. King & Queen Emblematical. Juno and Æolus. Christ making the Winds and Sea obey him. Three Academical Figures. And a Virgins Head.

5. Abigail bringing presents to David. Angels adoring the Creation. A Vestal towing a large Vessel. The Ascension of Christ. St. Peter enthron'd.

   NB – All these are by Pietro da Cortona and Ciro Ferri.

15. Gideon with the Fleece. Two Drawings suppos'd by Filippo Laura. Four of Romanelli amongst them.
   NB – The Drawings of Pietro da Cortona and Ciro Ferri are so similar that they are seldom distinguish'd.

___
44.

(p. 112)   Tom. II (= Inv. Nos. 4441–4480)

20. Martial and Religious or Popish Devices mix'd, The first Drawing a Design for a Clock and Ornaments for insides of Churches, Pallaces, and other Devices. Two Monumental.

5. Hind Standards of State Coaches.

1. Candlestick Ornaments. A Sketch of a Building on the back.

5. Various designs for Fountains.

4. Of Angels. Cherubs Heads & Angels supporting a Madonna's Picture.

5. Two from the Antique. A Study of Lyons. The Rape of the Sabines. A Design for a Fan. A Carnival Carr.

―――
40.

(p. 113)
P. CORTONA, CIRO FERRI, ROMANELLI,
SALVATOR ROSA &c.ª
(= Inv. Nos. 4481–4507, 0150–0152,
6120–6128, and 096)

1. The Ornamental Arms of the family of Barbarini.

1. An Ornamental design for the exposition of the Host.

11. A Virgin & Saints Angels &c.ª. J: Christ appearing to Mary Magdalen. Abraham and Isaac. A Sacrifice & emblematical above for a Coat of Arms. Paul preaching at Athens. An Altar with emblematical figures. Apotheosis of Hercules a design for a Cieling. The morning Star driving away Night. A Battle. V:M: & Saints. A Crucifixion.

5. Three emblematical. Two Evangelists St. Luke & St. Mark.

7. A Nativity. The Harvest, engrav'd by Spierre. Elijah with the Widows cruse of Oil. J:C: driving the Money changers out of the Temple. The beheading of St. Paul. The body of a dead Prince discover'd by the rest of the Army his Wife and friends. A Subject taken from the Revelations.

2. A Plan of a Building presented to the Pope. St. Peter and St. Paul appearing to a Pope, like the Story of St. Leo & Atilla.

3. By Romanelli, a Coriolanus. And a Duel in the presence of the Army. Camillus punishing the treacherous Schoolmaster.

10. Different sketches of Salvator Rosa.

―――
40.

(p. 114)   GIOVAN LORENZO BERNINO
Tom. I (= Inv. Nos. 5539–5589)

7. Portraits.

9. Compositions, some Historical.

8. The four Cardinal Virtues. The Study's of Angels for the Ciborio in the Chapel of the Sacrament at St. Peters Rome.

20. Of Cielings and Church as well as other Architectural Ornaments.

―――
50.

Tom. II (= Inv. Nos. 5590–5643)

11. Inside of Churches. The front of the Jesuits College at Rome. The Ciborio at St. Peters. And different Altars most of them in Rome.

11. An Equestrian Statue surrounded with Tophy's & Ornaments. The Monuments of Popes in St. Peters. And the other a Design for one, and seven others for different Monuments.

9. Two for Funeral Obsequies or Catafalcas. A first design for the Cathedra in St. Peters. One Altar one Monumental. Two Carrs. The Triumph. The Liberal Arts. Two the hind Standards of State Coaches.

7. Designs of Fountains in different parts near and at Rome.

4. The Elephant with the Obelisk on his Back in the Piazza della Minerva at Rome. And three Vases.

3. Two of Branched Candlesticks. And one Candlestick for the Churches.

9. Of Ornaments in Architecture.

―――
54.

(p. 128)   MODERNA SCHUOLA ROMANA
Tom. I (= Inv. Nos. 6713–6737)

10. Six of Gemignana. One of Luigi Garzi: Two of Mons.ºr Danielle and one of Lazzaro Baldi.

4. Four finish'd Drawings, in Red Chalk of some Scholar of Maratti's.

7. Of Pompeo Battoni & Steffano Pozzi.

4. Three of Pozzi and one of Turroni.

―――
25.

Tom. II (= Inv. Nos. 6738–6768)

30. Of Bacicia Galli, Lazzaro Baldi, Baglioni, &c.ª
―――

Tom. III (= Inv. Nos. 6769–6800)

26. Eight small Drawings of a good Scholar of P: da Cortona. Six Drawings of Palma, misplac'd in this Collection. The last Drawing but one is of Mola. all the rest are of Inferior Professors.

Tom. IV (= Inv. Nos. 6802–6827)

26. Guglielmo Burgognone a Cotempory of Carlo Maratti. Baccicia. Baldi. and others of inferior note.

CATALOGUE

Fig. 1

Cat. No. 2

Fig. 2

Cat. No. 1

CATALOGUE

FRANCESCO ALLEGRINI (1587–1663)
(attributed to)

1. MARTIN V ENTERING ROME (*Fig. 2*)   (6778)

226 × 501 mm. Pen and brown wash.

Mr. Philip Pouncey first called attention to the similarity of the style of drawing to that of Allegrini. The hypothesis that the drawing may be by him is supported by the fact that he painted a series of lunettes for the Palazzo Colonna in a style and with a scale of figures closely resembling the drawing. It is true that the lunettes illustrate scenes from Roman history, but the return of the Colonna pope, Martin V, to Rome might well have been considered as the subject for a painting in the Palazzo Colonna, even if the painting was never executed.

GIOVANNI BAGLIONI
(1571–1644)

2. ST. PAUL (*Fig. 1*)   (6764)

300 × 196 mm. Pen and brown wash, heightened with white, on brown paper. Inscribed: *Cavalir Baglione* on the step.

The Saint holds a sword, while behind him an angel appears holding a book.

According to a manuscript note in the Royal Library copy of Titi's *Descrizione* of 1763 (p. 24), Baglioni painted figures of St. Peter and St. Paul over the altarpiece in S. Marta (near St. Peter's). Baglioni himself (*Vite*, Rome, 1642, p. 402) only speaks of the altarpiece which he painted, and which was presumably replaced by Calandrucci's in the restoration undertaken by Clement XI.

LAZZARO BALDI
(1623–1703)

3. THE VISION OF ST. JOHN ON PATMOS (*Fig. 3*)   (5952)

333 × 211 mm. Pen and brown wash, heightened with white, on brown paper.

Study for the painting in S. Giovanni in Oleo, painted c. 1658 (cf. Waterhouse, p. 46).

4. THE MARTYRDOM OF A ROMAN SOLDIER   (6721)
(? St. Sebastian)

343 × 228 mm. Pen and brown wash, heightened with white. Inscribed: *Lorenzo B* and *Lazaro Baldi*. Squared.

The Saint, wearing only a loin-cloth, is being bound to a stake. His armour, of which he has just been stripped, lies at his feet. A boy on the left shows him a bow and arrow in a threatening manner, and another, on the right, holds a second bow. In the background the courtyard of a Roman palace. The drawing fits the Martyrdom of St. Sebastian, except for the fact that it should take place in a field, not in a palace.

The similarity of style with No. 3 supports the attribution to Baldi given in the old inscription.

5. A SAINT IN PRAYER ACCOMPANIED BY PUTTI   (5953)

213 × 162 mm. Pen and brown wash over black chalk.

Inv. A, p. 146, as Baldi.

The style is consistent with No. 3.

Fig. 3   Cat. No. 3

PIETRO SANTI BARTOLI (c.1635–1700)
(attributed to)

5a. A ROMAN CUIRASS   (4390)

250 × 182 mm. Pen and brown ink.

Inv. A, p. 110: Carlo Maratti.

Probably after the Antique. The attribution is based on the similarity to Bartoli's known drawings after the Antique, for instance those in the Vittoria volume at Windsor (A 22).

POMPEO BATONI
(1708–87)

6. STUDIES FOR THE HEAD OF ST. PETER   (5375)

218 × 375 mm. Black, white and red chalk on grey-brown paper.

Two studies of a head like that of the Saint in the *Fall of Simon Magus* in S. Maria degli Angeli, Rome, both seen from a slightly different view-point from the painting.

7. FIGURE STUDIES (*Fig. 4*)   (6731)

227 × 187 mm. Red chalk on ochre-tinted paper. Inscribed: *studi di Pompeo Batoni*.

Three studies of the nude and one of drapery. The figure at the top left is close to the Polyphemus in the painting of *Polyphemus, Acis and Galatea*, signed and dated 1761, which in 1935 was in the V. Larby collection, Stockholm. The crouching figure in the bottom right-hand corner is close in pose to the Galatea in the same painting.

8. STUDIES OF A BEARDED MAN   (6732)

210 × 167 mm. Red and white chalk on ochre-tinted paper.

Inv. A, p. 128. From a group of drawings by Stefano Pozzo and Batoni.
Study of the head and a smaller one of the upper half of the body. The larger head is close to the St. Marinus in the *Allegory of the Republic of S. Marino* in the Pinacoteca at S. Marino (repr. in C. Ricci, *San Marino (Italia Artistica)*, Bergamo, 1903, p. 45). The smaller study is for the *St. Bartholomew*, formerly in the Galleria Merenda, Forlì. This information was kindly supplied by Mr. Anthony Clark.

POMPEO BATONI (attributed to)

9. HEAD OF A GIRL   (6728)

373 × 245 mm. Black, white and red chalk on ochre-tinted paper.

Inv. A, p. 128. From a group of drawings by Stefano Pozzo and Batoni.
The technique is close to that of Nos. 7 and 8, and the head is not unlike that of Vice in the *Choice of Hercules*, painted in 1742 and engraved by C. Faucci after Batoni (repr. in E. Panofsky, *Hercules am Scheidewege*, Leipzig, 1930, Pl. LVI, Fig. 84).

10. HEAD OF A YOUNG WOMAN   (5370)

273 × 187 mm. Black, white and red chalk on ochre-tinted paper.

The technique is typical of Batoni as shown in No. 7.

Fig. 4   Cat. No. 7

11. AN ALLEGORY OF MUSIC (*Plate 65*)   (6733)

230 × 253 mm. Red chalk.

Inv. A, p. 128. From a group of drawings by Stefano Pozzo and Batoni.
On the left Apollo sits on a rock. Below him are two putti, one holding a caduceus, the other a bow. A woman kneels before him and offers a sheet of music. Mercury flies down from above with the musical instrument which he has made from the shell of the tortoise. On the right Mars approaches with a gesture of humility.
When this catalogue was already in proof, Mr. Anthony Clark suggested an attribution to Bonatti for this drawing.

12. ACADEMY   (1332)

350 × 269 mm. Red chalk.

From the Domenichino volume, but the particular type of cross-hatching is like that used by Batoni. The drawing may, however, be earlier.

NICCOLO BERETTONI
(1637–82)

13. ST. ANTHONY ABOUT TO CROSS A RIVER IN A BOAT

190 × 168 mm. Red chalk.   (4098)

Study for a painting by Berettoni in the church of S. Antonio Abbate in Pesaro.

14. THE FLAGELLATION OF ST. ANDREW   (01123)

396 × 615 mm. Red and white chalk. Squared.

Inv. A, p. 158, as N. Berettoni.

After Domenichino's fresco in S. Gregorio al Celio, Rome. A copy by Berettoni of the companion fresco, Reni's *St. Andrew led to execution*, is catalogued by O. Kurz among the Bolognese drawings (No.386).

NICCOLO BERETTONI (attributed to)

15. STUDY OF A NUDE   (4134)

170 × 266 mm. Red and white chalk on grey paper.

Inv. A, p. 107, as Maratta.

Probably connected with a fresco in the Villa Falconieri, Frascati, attributed to Berettoni (cf. Waterhouse, p. 48).

GIOVANNI LORENZO BERNINI
(1598–1680)

Inventory A describes two volumes containing 105 mounted drawings ascribed to Bernini (Nos.5539–5643), in which a further ten drawings (Nos.5529–5538) were loosely inserted. Of these a large number are only very generally connected with his style and are here catalogued in the sections dealing with artists such as Gaulli and Schor, who were directly influenced by him, or among the anonymous drawings. There remains, however, an impressive body of drawings, both original and from the studio, of which many are connected with executed works. If these have been given somewhat summary treatment below, the reason is that they have been so fully studied in the work of Brauer and Wittkower (*Die Zeichnungen des Gianlorenzo Bernini*, Berlin, 1931) that it seemed useless to repeat their arguments in full, the more so because these arguments are not intelligible without a consideration of other drawings not in the Royal Collection.

The following entries do, however, include certain drawings not mentioned by Brauer and Wittkower. In some cases this is because the drawings were concealed in the miscellaneous volumes and had not been connected with the name of Bernini. This category includes a black and red chalk drawing of *David with the head of Goliath* (No.59), in the manner of the portrait drawings, a *Study of a nude* (No.63), and, most important of all, a fine drawing of a *Fountain of Neptune* (No.42), which seems to be connected with the Piazza Navona fountains.

Certain other drawings must have been known to Brauer and Wittkower, since they come from the main Bernini series, but are not mentioned by them. In many cases these are studio drawings of no great importance, but one, for the Porta Santa (No.36), is at any rate in part from the hand of Bernini himself.

In other cases the editors have ventured to differ from the attributions made by Brauer and Wittkower, usually in being more generous in their attributions to Bernini himself of drawings hitherto regarded as studio works. Such changes are noted in each individual case, but the editors are authorised by Professor Wittkower, who has

kindly read this section of the catalogue, to say that in general he is in agreement with their suggestions, though he continues to maintain his doubts about the attribution to Bernini himself of Nos.52, 61 and 62.

1. Drawings connected with known works

ARICCIA, Chiesa Collegiata

Designed and built by Bernini between 1662 and 1664 (cf. Wittkower, *Bernini*, p. 224, and G. Incisa della Rocchetta, 'Notizie sulla fabbrica della Chiesa Collegiata di Ariccia', *Rivista del Reale Istituto d'Archeologia e Storia dell' Arte*, i, 1929, pp. 349–92).

16. STUDY FOR THE DECORATION OF THE DOME   (5566)

273 × 212 mm. Pen and brown wash over black chalk.

Lit.: Brauer and Wittkower, pp. 10 note 6, 125, and Pl. 169c.

17. STUDIES OF PUTTI FOR THE DOME   (5570)

269 × 253 mm. Black chalk and pen with brown ink.

Lit.: Brauer and Wittkower, pp. 8 note 6, 125, 140, 141, and Pl. 174b.

The sheet also contains sketches for the Silva Chapel in S. Isidoro, Rome (1663). Brauer and Wittkower assign both these drawings to a pupil, probably Paolo Naldini, who was responsible for the stucco figures in the dome, but No. 17 seems to be by Bernini himself, and although the greater part of No. 16 appears to be by a pupil, the putti are far more freely drawn and were probably added by Bernini.

CASTEL GANDOLFO, S. Tommaso da Villanueva
HIGH ALTAR

Executed 1660–61, the stucco figures by Raggi (cf. Brauer and Wittkower, p. 119, and Wittkower, *Bernini*, p. 223).

18. STUDY FOR THE ALTAR   (5615)

245 × 181 mm. Pen and brown wash, with some black chalk in the central medallion.

Lit.: Brauer and Wittkower, pp. 10 note 6, 119, and Pl. 169d; R. Pane, *Bernini architetto*, Venice, 1952, Pl. 124 (wrongly said to be in the Vatican Library).

A studio drawing.

CASTEL GANDOLFO, Papal Palace, Garden Gate

Probably built c.1636–37 (cf. Brauer and Wittkower, p. 31).

19. DESIGN FOR THE GATE   (5588)

155 × 150 mm. Black chalk and pen with brown ink.

Lit.: Brauer and Wittkower, pp.31, 32, and Pl. 14b.

ROME, S. Lorenzo in Lucina, Cappella Fonseca

Executed on Bernini's designs, probably c.1663–64 (cf. Wittkower, *Bernini*, p. 236).

20. DESIGN FOR THE ALTAR   (5599)

399 × 265 mm. Pen and bistre wash over black chalk.

Scale at bottom.

Lit.: Wittkower, *Bernini*, p. 236, and Fig. 91.

A studio drawing.

ROME, S. Maria Maggiore
TOMB OF ALEXANDER VII

Clement IX conceived the idea of placing his own tomb and that of his predecessor, Alexander VII (d. 1667), as a pair in the new *tribuna* of S. Maria Maggiore, and commissioned Bernini to prepare designs. In 1670, after the death of Clement IX, the project was abandoned and the heirs of Alexander returned to the original scheme for putting the tomb in St. Peter's (cf. No. 35).

DESIGNS FOR THE TOMB

21. 400 × 268 mm. Pen and bistre wash over black chalk. (5604)

Lit.: Voss, *Archiv für Kunstgeschichte*, ii, 1914–15, Pl. 160 (left); Brauer and Wittkower, pp. 168, 169, 175, and Pls. 129a, 130.

Exh.: Royal Academy, London, 1950–51, No.392.

22. 146 × 126 mm. Black chalk. (5609)

Lit.: Brauer and Wittkower, p. 168, and Pl. 129b.

ROME, St. Peter's
BALDACCHINO

Commissioned in 1624 and completed in 1635 (cf. Brauer and Wittkower, pp. 19–22, and Wittkower, *Bernini*, pp. 187 f.).

23. DESIGN FOR THE UPPER HALF OF A COLUMN (5635)

496 × 215 mm. Pen and brown wash.

Lit.: Brauer and Wittkower, p. 21 note 1.

24. DESIGN FOR THE ENTABLATURE (5636)

The drawing cut out in an irregular shape 369 × 330 mm. Set in a sheet 392 × 341 mm. Pen and brown wash over black chalk.

The decoration of the frieze with a sun is on a separate piece of paper stuck on the sheet.

Lit.: Brauer and Wittkower, p. 21 note 1.

25. DESIGN FOR THE CANOPY (5637)

339 × 452 mm. Pen and bistre wash over black chalk.

Lit.: Brauer and Wittkower, p. 21 note 1.

All three studio drawings.

ROME, St. Peter's
CATHEDRA PETRI

The decision to create a worthy setting for the Chair of St. Peter was made in 1656. In the next year a first model was produced. In the execution (1660–66) the project was greatly enlarged (cf. Brauer and Wittkower, pp. 104–110, and Wittkower, *Bernini*, pp. 219–223).

26. STUDY FOR THE FIRST DESIGN (5614)

241 × 145 mm. Pen and brown wash over black chalk. Inscribed: *Del Cavalier Gio: Lorenzo Bernino.*

Lit.: Brauer and Wittkower, pp. 10 note 4, 105, 106, 139, 169, 171, and Pl. 166a; R. Battaglia, *La Cattedra Berniniana di San Pietro*, Rome, 1943, pp. 54, 57, 73, 78, 80, 84, 97, and Pl. IV; H. Kauffmann, *Münchner Jahrbuch der bildenden Kunst*, Dritte Folge, vi, 1955, p. 239; H. von Einem, *Nachrichten der Akademie der Wissenschaften . . . Göttingen, Phil.-hist. Klasse*, 1955, p. 104, Fig. 5; Wittkower, *Bernini*, p. 219.

Exh.: Royal Academy, London, 1950–51, No.383.

Studio drawing for the model of 1657.

27. STUDY FOR THE GLORY (5564)

373 × 273 mm. Black chalk and pen, with brown ink. Scale at the bottom.

Lit.: Brauer and Wittkower, pp. 9 note 3, 107–109, and Pl. 79; R. Battaglia, *La Cattedra Berniniana di San Pietro*, Rome, 1943, pp. 55, 117 f.; Wittkower, *Bernini*, p. 221.

Drawing for the oval window in the first scheme.

ROME, St. Peter's
ALTAR OF THE
CAPPELLA DEL SS. SACRAMENTO

Urban VIII commissioned Bernini to design an altar for the Cappella del SS. Sacramento in 1629, but the project was not carried out. The existing altar was designed for Alexander VII in 1658–61 and executed in 1673–75 (cf. Brauer and Wittkower, p. 174, and Wittkower, *Bernini*, p. 240), but Innocent X seems also to have commissioned a design from an artist in the circle of Bernini (cf. No. 32).

28. STUDY FOR THE RIGHT-HAND KNEELING ANGEL (*Plate 16*) (5560)

144 × 168 mm. Black chalk and brown wash, on discoloured white paper.

Lit.: Brauer and Wittkower, pp. 174, 175, and Pl. 136b.

Exh.: Burlington Fine Arts Club, London, 1925, No.32; Royal Academy, London, 1950–51, No.390.

STUDIES FOR THE LEFT-HAND KNEELING ANGEL

29. 141 × 152 mm. Oval. Cut and made up on the left. Black chalk. (5561)

Lit.: Brauer and Wittkower, pp. 10 note 3, 173, 174 note 4, and Pl. 132b.

Exh.: Royal Academy, London, 1950–51, No.393.

30. 153 × 136 mm. Pen and brown wash over black chalk, on discoloured white paper. (*Plate 15*) (5562)

Lit.: Brauer and Wittkower, p. 175, and Pl. 136a.

No. 29 shows one of the angels in the first stage; Nos. 28 and 30 show the two figures in poses approaching their final form.

31. DESIGN FOR THE WHOLE ALTAR AND CANDLESTICKS

510 × 745 mm. Pen and grey wash. (11592)

Lit.: Brauer and Wittkower, pp. 173, 175, and Pl. 195c.

This design has the arms of Clement X (1670–76), by whose Pontificate the altar itself was finished. It shows a project for completing the scheme with candlesticks, two variants for which are shown on tabs.

32. DESIGN FOR THE WHOLE ALTAR   (5596)

502 × 374 mm. Black chalk.

Lit.: Brauer and Wittkower, p. 174 note 1.

This drawing has a papal coat of arms which, though difficult to decipher, must be that of Innocent X. The drawing shows the model of a church with four towers and a dome, in the centre of which is a monstrance. The model is supported by figures of a bishop and an angel. It is probably, as Brauer and Wittkower suggest, connected with the altar of the SS. Sacramento in St. Peter's, though there is no record of Innocent X having commissioned a design for it. The drawing comes from the Bernini volumes, but neither the architecture of the model, nor the draughtsmanship of the figures is very close to his style. On the basis of the arms it can be dated to the years 1644–55.

ROME, St. Peter's
TOMB OF URBAN VIII

The tomb was first planned in 1627, but was not completed until 1647 (cf. Brauer and Wittkower, pp. 22–25, and Wittkower, *Bernini*, pp. 193 f.).

33. DESIGN FOR THE WHOLE MONUMENT   (5602)

534 × 319 mm. Pen and brown wash over black chalk.

Lit.: Brauer and Wittkower, pp. 10 note 6, 11, 23, and Pl. 151.

A studio drawing for the whole monument according to the first project, probably dating from 1627–8.

34. STUDY FOR THE FIGURE OF THE POPE   (5558)

200 × 188 mm. Oval. Red chalk.

Exact copy of the statue.

ROME, St. Peter's
TOMB OF ALEXANDER VII

Commissioned by Alexander but executed after his death, between 1671 and 1678 (cf. Brauer and Wittkower, pp. 168–71, and Wittkower, *Bernini*, pp. 238–40).

35. DESIGN FOR THE WHOLE MONUMENT   (5603)

440 × 307 mm. Pen and bistre wash over black chalk. Scale at the bottom.

Lit.: Voss, *Archiv für Kunstgeschichte*, ii, 1914–15, Pl. 160 (right); Brauer and Wittkower, p. 169, and Pl. 183.

Exh.: *17th Century Art*, Royal Academy, London, 1938, No. 422.

Studio drawing of unusually good quality.

ROME, St. Peter's
PORTA SANTA

A new inscription replaced the old one on the occasion of the Holy Year of 1650.

Fig. 5   Cat. No. 36

36. DESIGN FOR THE DOOR *(Fig. 5)*   (5589)

376 × 202 mm. Pen and brown wash, the cross in red water-colour. A scale at the bottom. A tab (136 × 179 mm.) with the new inscription over the door. The drawing is inscribed: URBANUS · VIII PONTIFEX MAXIMUS PORTAM · SANCTAM RESERAVIT · ET · CLAUSIT ANNO · IUBILEI · M · DC · XXV CLEMENS · VIII · PONTIFEX · MAXIMUS HANC · SANCTAM. PORTAM APERTAM · ET · CLAUSAM · A · GREGORIO · XIII · PONTIFICE · MAX · ANNO · IUBILEI · M · DLXXV APERUIT · ET · CLAUSIT ANNO · IUBILEI · M · D · C. The tab is inscribed: INNOCENTIUS · X · PONT · MAX PORTAM · HANC · SACTᾱ RESERVATAM ET · CLAUSAM AB. URBANO · VIII· PONT · MAX ANNO IUBILEI · M · DCXXV APERUIT · ET · CLAUSIT ANNO IUB · M · DC · L.

The lower drawing, which is by a member of Bernini's studio, shows the state of the Porta Santa before the Holy Year 1650. The tab, which appears to be by Bernini himself, shows the inscription which was to replace the earlier one after the opening and closing of the door by Innocent X in that year. The decoration round the inscription includes the dove and the fleur-de-lys of the Pamphili family.

ROME, Palazzo Barberini
ELEPHANT WITH OBELISK

Bernini planned a monument with an elephant supporting an obelisk for the garden of the Palazzo Barberini. It was never executed and the idea was later adapted to the monument outside the Minerva erected under Alexander VII.

37. DESIGN FOR THE WHOLE MONUMENT   (5628)
273 × 116 mm. Pen and brown wash over black chalk.
Lit.: Brauer and Wittkower, pp. 10 note 2, 145–7, 150, and Pl. 14a.
The drawing can be connected with the Barberini monument on account of what appear to be bees at the top of the obelisk. The style also indicates an early date.

ROME, Piazza Barberini
FONTANA DEL TRITONE

Probably executed in the 1630's (cf. Wittkower, *Bernini*, p. 195).

38. STUDY FOR THE WHOLE DESIGN   (5626)
319 × 263 mm. Pen and brown wash.
Lit.: Brauer and Wittkower, pp. 10 note 3, 35, 36, 47, and Pl. 152c; Wittkower, *Bernini*, p. 195.
Exh.: Burlington Fine Arts Club, London, 1925, No. 31.
Classified by Brauer and Wittkower as a studio drawing, but the pen work may be original.

ROME, Piazza Navona
FOUNTAIN OF THE FOUR RIVERS

Executed between 1648 and 1651 (cf. Brauer and Wittkower, pp. 47–50; R. Battaglia, *La Cattedra Berniniana di S. Pietro*, Rome, 1943, p. 246; R. Pane, *Bernini architetto*, Venice, 1952, Pl. 94; and Wittkower, *Bernini*, p. 210).

39. STUDY FOR THE WHOLE DESIGN   (5621)
333 × 436 mm. Black chalk with brown wash, the water is touched with blue.
Lit.: Voss, *Jahrbuch der preussischen Kunstsammlungen*, xxxi, 1910, p. 110, Fig. 6; Brauer and Wittkower, pp. 10 note 2, 47, 48, and Pl. 27.
The drawing shows the design at an early stage, just after that given in a drawing at Ariccia (Brauer and Wittkower, Pls. 25b, 26).

ROME, Piazza Navona
FONTANA DEL MORO

Designed and executed between 1652 and 1655 (cf. Brauer and Wittkower, pp. 50–53, and Wittkower, *Bernini*, pp. 215 ff.).

STUDIES FOR THE WHOLE DESIGN (*Plate 11*)
40. 396 × 245 mm. Pen and brown wash, on brown-tinted paper, the water in blue wash.   (5625)
Lit.: Voss, *Jahrbuch der preussischen Kunstsammlungen*, xxxi, 1910, p. 107, Fig. 3; Brauer and Wittkower, pp. 10 note 2, 51, 52, and Pl. 32; R. Pane, *Bernini architetto*, Venice, 1952, Pl. 108; Wittkower, *Bernini*, p. 215.
Exh.: Royal Academy, London, 1950–51, No.379.
The drawing shows the first design for the fountain (1652).

41. 246 × 206 mm. Pen and brown wash. (*Plate 10*) (5623)
Lit.: Brauer and Wittkower, pp. 10 note 2, 51–53, and Pl. 33; L. Grassi, *Disegni del Bernini*, Bergamo, 1944, Pl. 17; R. Pane, *Bernini architetto*, Venice, 1952, Pl. 87; Wittkower, *Bernini*, p. 216.
Exh.: Burlington Fine Arts Club, London, 1925, No.28; *17th Century Art*, Royal Academy, London, 1938, No.441; Royal Academy, London, 1950–51, No.382.
This drawing represents the second stage of the design, with tritons and dolphins.

ROME, Piazza Navona
FOUNTAIN OF NEPTUNE

42. DESIGN FOR THE WHOLE FOUNTAIN (*Plate 12*)
                                                      (10758)
296 × 390 mm. Pen and brown wash, on brown paper.

This drawing, which was unknown to Brauer and Wittkower, seems to show that a Fountain of Neptune was envisaged in the Piazza Navona. The basin as shown in the present drawing has the same form as that of the Fontana del Moro, the only difference being that the bays between the semi-circular basins are simple right-angles, as opposed to the more complex form of Giacomo della Porta's construction. It also has four heads which spit water into an outer basin, as in the Fontana del Moro, though in the latter they are at the corners, whereas in the drawing they are in the semi-circular bays. The design further corresponds with the Moro in that the central group shows a figure on a shell, supported by sea monsters, with the papal arms on the front, and in the basin around it are four tritons blowing on conches.

From the similarity of No.42 to the Fontana del Moro we may conclude that it was either an alternative design for this fountain, or a project for a second fountain to balance it at the other end of the Piazza Navona. The documents about the Fontana del Moro, published by Fraschetti, are fairly complete, and they make no mention of any project for introducing a figure of Neptune. There is, however, at Leipzig (No.32–76; cf. Brauer and Wittkower, p. 52 note 2) a studio drawing showing a figure of Neptune, pointing with his right hand and holding a water-pot in his left, in a pose strongly reminiscent of No.42, which is inscribed in a seventeenth-century hand: *à Piazza Navona in luogo del Tritone*. This would seem to imply that the Neptune was an alternative to the Moro.

On the other hand, it is extremely probable that the Pope planned to make a second fountain, which is essential to the symmetry of the scheme. In fact, a fountain with Neptune as a central figure and Tritons round him was erected in 1878 by Antonio della Bitta and Gregorio Zappalà, and one may wonder whether at that date a document was known, or a tradition existed, that a second fountain of Neptune was originally planned. The basin had already been constructed under Gregory XIII (cf. *Roma*, 1939, p. 67, and *Piazza Navona, Catalogo a cura di Elsa Gerlini*, Rome, 1943, p. 96).

ROME, Vatican
SCALA REGIA

Designed and executed between 1660 and 1666 (cf. Brauer and Wittkower, pp. 88–96).

43. DECORATION OF CEILING AT LANDING   (5565)

274 × 202 mm. Pen and brown wash.

Lit.: Brauer and Wittkower, p. 96 note 2.

A copy after the actual decoration by a member of Bernini's studio.

SASSUOLO (Modena), Palazzo degli Estensi
FOUNTAIN OF NEPTUNE

STUDIES FOR THE CENTRAL GROUP (*Plate 13*)

44. 347 × 238 mm. Black chalk.   (5624)

Verso: Design for the same fountain.

Lit.: Voss, *Jahrbuch der preussischen Kunstsammlungen*, xxxi, 1910, p. 117, Fig. 16; Brauer and Wittkower, pp. 9 note 4, 53, and Pls. 36, 38; Donati, *L'Urbe*, ii, 1941, p. 11; Wittkower, *Bernini*, p. 243; Wittkower, Catalogue of the exhibition *Great Master Drawings of Seven Centuries*, Knoedler, New York, 1959, p. 43.

Exh.: *17th Century Art*, Royal Academy, London, 1938, No. 445; Royal Academy, London, 1950–51, No.391; *Great Master Drawings of Seven Centuries*, Knoedler Galleries, New York, 1959, No.34, Pl. 36.

45. 340 × 264 mm. Black chalk. (*Plate 14*)   (5627)

Lit.: Brauer and Wittkower, pp. 9 note 4, 53, and Pl. 37.

Exh.: Burlington Fine Arts Club, 1925, No.27; Royal Academy, London, 1950–51, No.381.

These drawings have been identified by U. Donati (*loc. cit.*) as being preparations for a fountain executed by Raggi from Bernini's designs at Sassuolo.

2. Drawings connected with works no longer surviving

46. PORTRAIT OF ALEXANDER VII   (5532)

255 × 196 mm. Red chalk.

Lit.: Brauer and Wittkower, p. 157 note 5; V. Martinelli, *I ritratti di Pontefici di G. L. Bernini*, Rome, 1956, p. 44, Pl. 20.

Probably a copy of one of Bernini's busts of the Pope. The nearest seems to be that in the Muñoz collection, Rome (repr. Wittkower, *Bernini*, p. 185, Fig. 23).

47. DESIGN FOR A LOOKING-GLASS FOR THE QUEEN OF SWEDEN   (5586)

230 × 188 mm. Pen and brown wash over black chalk. In-scribed: *Disegno del Cavalier Gio. Lorenzo Bernino per uno specchio per la Regina di Suetia.*

Lit.: Brauer and Wittkower, pp. 151, 171; Wittkower, *Bernini*, p. 204, and Fig. 51.

Probably made about 1656. Brauer and Wittkower ascribe the drawing to a studio hand. In his later book Wittkower is more optimistic and only says that 'there is some doubt as to its authenticity'.

The mirror itself was seen and drawn by Tessin (R. Jorghson, *Tessin*, Stockholm, 1930, i, Fig. 40). It differed considerably from the drawing in the disposition of the drapery, which in the mirror itself covers more of the actual surface of the glass than in the drawing.

DESIGNS FOR THE CATAFALQUE OF CARLO BARBERINI

48. 485 × 261 mm. Pen and brown wash, on discoloured white paper. A scale at the bottom.   (5613)

49. 251 × 193 mm. Pen and brown wash.   (5612)

Lit.: Brauer and Wittkower, p. 162 note 6.

Designed in 1630 for the funeral of Carlo Barberini in S. Maria d'Aracoeli (cf. Fraschetti, *Il Bernini*, Milan, 1904, pp. 93 f.). The drawings, which are both studio works, show an open circular building with projecting coupled columns.

DESIGNS FOR A CHARIOT FOR AGOSTINO CHIGI

50. 485 × 369 mm. Pen and brown wash over black chalk, on discoloured white paper. Inscribed: *VIRTUS TERMINAT ASTRIS.*   (5617)

Lit.: Brauer and Wittkower, pp. 10 note 4, 137, and Pl. 172a.

Exh.: Royal Academy, London, 1950–51, No.384.

51. 366 × 251 mm. Pen and brown wash over black chalk, on discoloured white paper. Inscribed: *Questo mi dispiacie meno.*   (5618)

Lit.: Brauer and Wittkower, pp. 10 note 4, 137, and Pl. 172b.

Exh.: Royal Academy, London, 1950–51, No.385.

Designs for a chariot made for the Carnival of 1658 (cf. Incisa della Rocchetta, *Rivista di studi e di vita romana*, vi, 1928, pp. 271–6). In both a winged figure, holding the star and the oak-branch of the Chigi arms, sits surrounded by allegorical figures of the arts. Classed by Brauer and Wittkower as studio drawings, but possibly original. Another drawing for the chariot is in the Chigi collection (cf. Fraschetti, p. 256).

52. TWO STANDING ANGELS HOLDING A MONSTRANCE

141 × 170 mm. Pen and brown wash.   (5559)

Lit.: Brauer and Wittkower, p. 172 note 2.

Connected with Bernini's design for angels carrying a monstrance at Leipzig (repr. Brauer and Wittkower, Pl. 131a). Classed by Brauer and Wittkower as a studio work, but perhaps an original.

Fig. 6   Cat. No. 59

3. Drawings not connected with known works

53. SELF-PORTRAIT   (5540)

410 × 267 mm. Black, red and white chalk on buff paper.

Lit.: Brauer and Wittkower, p. 16, and Pl. 9; Wittkower, *Burlington Magazine*, xciii, 1951, p. 55; V. Martinelli, *Commentari*, i, 1950, p. 180.

Exh.: Royal Academy, London, 1950–51, No.380.

The identification of the sitter as Bernini is open to doubt.

54. SELF-PORTRAIT (*Plate 9*)   (5539)

413 × 271 mm. Black and white chalk on buff paper.

Lit.: Brauer and Wittkower, p. 17, and Pl. 108; V. Martinelli, *Commentari*, i, 1950, p. 182; R. Wittkower, *Burlington Magazine*, xciii, 1951, pp. 52, 55; Wittkower, *Bernini*, frontispiece.

Exh.: Burlington Fine Arts Club, London, 1925, No.29; *17th Century Art*, Royal Academy, London, 1938, No.443; Fitzwilliam Museum, Cambridge, 1959, No.7.

Probably executed c.1665.

55. PORTRAIT OF A BOY (*Plate 8*)   (5543)

205 × 177 mm. Black, red and white chalk on buff paper.

Lit.: Brauer and Wittkower, p. 14, and Pl. 1; L. Grassi, *Disegni del Bernini*, Bergamo, 1944, Pl. 3; L. Grassi, *Bernini Pittore*, Rome, 1945, p. 24, and Fig. 22; V. Martinelli, *Commentari*, i, 1950, p. 179; R. Wittkower, *Burlington Magazine*, xciii, 1951, p. 55; F. Zeri, 'Gian Lorenzo Bernini: Un

marmo dimenticato e un disegno', *Paragone*, No.115, 1959, p. 63.

Exh.: Burlington Fine Arts Club, London, 1925, No.30; *17th Century Art*, Royal Academy, London, 1938, No.440; Royal Academy, London, 1950–51, No.389.

Said by Brauer and Wittkower to be a self-portrait.

56. PORTRAIT OF A MAN   (5530)

390 × 244 mm. Black and red chalk on buff paper.

Lit.: Brauer and Wittkower, p. 14, and Pl. 3; R. Wittkower, *Burlington Magazine*, xciii, 1951, p. 52.

This is said by Brauer and Wittkower to be a self-portrait, but the features do not conform to those portraits which certainly represent the artist. As these authors point out, the drawing is of a quality inferior to the other portrait drawings and it may be a copy.

57. PORTRAIT OF A MAN   (5542)

206 × 154 mm. Black, red and white chalk on buff paper.

Lit.: Brauer and Wittkower, pp. 16, 156, and Pl. 17; V. Martinelli, *Commentari*, i, 1950, p. 181; R. Wittkower, *Burlington Magazine*, xciii, 1951, p. 55.

Exh.: Royal Academy, London, 1950–51, No.387.

This is said by Brauer and Wittkower to be a self-portrait, but the suggestion is withdrawn by Wittkower in his later article. The drawing bears some resemblance to the features of Cassiano dal Pozzo.

58. PORTRAIT OF A MAN   (5541)

327 × 244 mm. Black, red and white chalk on buff paper.

Lit.: Brauer and Wittkower, p. 156, and Pl. 126; V. Martinelli, *Commentari*, i, 1950, pp. 179, 181.

59. DAVID WITH THE HEAD OF GOLIATH (*Fig. 6*) (4346)

257 × 211 mm. Black and red chalk on discoloured white paper. Damaged and patched on the right.

From the Maratta volumes.

Typical of Bernini's manner of using black and red chalks. Its presence in the Maratta volumes may be explained by the fact that he owned it.

60. SEATED NUDE SEEN FROM BEHIND   (5537)

562 × 422 mm. Red and white chalk. Inscribed: *Cav^{re}. Bernini.*

Lit.: Brauer and Wittkower, p. 10, and Pl. 119; V. Martinelli, *Commentari*, i, 1950, p. 175.

61. DESIGN FOR THE TOMB OF A BISHOP   (5606)

252 × 264 mm., with rounded top. Pen and brown wash on brown paper.

Lit.: Brauer and Wittkower, p. 172, and Pl. 185b.

Brauer and Wittkower class this with No.73 as a studio drawing, but it is of much finer quality than the other drawing and may be by Bernini himself.

Fig. 7   Cat. No. 62

62. DESIGN FOR A TOMB OF AN ECCLESIASTIC (*Fig. 7*)
(5605)

373 × 224 mm. Pen and bistre wash, on discoloured white paper.

The drawing shows a bearded man in ecclesiastical dress, seated in a sort of loge, turned presumably towards the altar, with one hand to his breast and the other resting on a cushion. Below a tablet with indications of an inscription and a winged skull. Above a blank coat of arms. The design is related in general terms to the side groups in the Cappella Cornaro in S. Maria della Vittoria (c.1645–52) and the tombs in Cappella Raimondi in S. Pietro in Montorio (1638–48). It probably dates, therefore, from the 1640's.

GIOVANNI LORENZO BERNINI
(attributed to)

63. SEATED MALE NUDE SEEN FROM BEHIND   (0251)

419 × 260 mm. Red and white chalk.

The drawing is said to have had the name of P. F. Mola on the mount, but it is quite unlike him in style, and the close similarity to No.60 makes an ascription to Bernini very probable.

GIOVANNI LORENZO BERNINI
(studio of)

64. TRIUMPH OF THE CHURCH   (5585)

289 × 215 mm. Pen and brown wash, on brown-washed paper.

Lit.: Brauer and Wittkower, pp. 10 note 4, 139, and Pl. 173b.

A figure of the papacy sits on the top of a globe, supported by flames, and is adored by two figures who offer her crowns. She holds an oak-branch, no doubt an allusion to the arms of Alexander VII. Perhaps a design for a coach, and probably executed c.1660.

65. CHRIST TRIUMPHANT   (5584)

180 × 149 mm. Pen and brown wash, heightened with white.

Lit.: Brauer and Wittkower, pp. 10 note 4, 139, and Pl. 173a.

Christ sits enthroned in the centre of a radiance and borne up by the four symbols of the Evangelists. Studio drawing, probably dating from the 1660's.

GIOVANNI LORENZO BERNINI
(follower of)

66. DESIGN FOR A CANDLESTICK WITH THE ARMS OF ALEXANDER VII   (5634)

546 × 204 mm. Pen and brown ink.

DESIGNS FOR A RELIQUARY

67. 250 × 140 mm. Pen and brown ink over black chalk.
(5610)

The top of the drawing is restored.

68. 267 × 142 mm. Pen and brown ink over black chalk.
(5611)

The designs consist of two putti, sitting back to back on a casket and supporting an oval frame decorated with palm-leaves.

69. DESIGN FOR A RELIQUARY   (5587)

195 × 250 mm. Pen and brown wash.

Two standing angels carry between them a casket on which stand two putti with a wreath and palm-leaves.

70. GOD THE FATHER   (5557)

227 × 358 mm. Red chalk, on faded white paper.

The figure faces left with outstretched hand in the act of creation.

71. RECUMBENT MALE NUDE   (4911)

291 × 388 mm. Torn and made up round three edges. Red chalk, heightened with white.

From the Sacchi volumes.

Near the manner of Bernini and in no way connected with Sacchi.

72. STANDING MALE NUDE   (5529)

362 × 248 mm. Red chalk on buff paper, heightened with white.

73. DESIGN FOR A TOMB OF A BISHOP   (5607)

302 × 174 mm. Pen and brown wash over black chalk. Inscribed: *Disegno fatto dal Cav^{re}. Gio: Lorenzo Bernino di età d'anni 81 per uno delli Depositi della Cappella che doveva fare il Cardinal Cibo al Popolo.*

Lit.: Brauer and Wittkower, p. 171, and Pl. 185a.

It is possible that the drawing may be connected with an early scheme for the Cappella Cibò in S. Maria del Popolo, but it is only connected with Bernini in the most general way.

74. DESIGN FOR AN ALTAR   (11593)

741 × 469 mm. Pen and brown wash over black chalk.

The design shows a painting of the Virgin and Child carried by two angels under a baldacchino. Below another angel carries the Host. Not connected with any known work by Bernini, but by an artist much influenced by his style.

DESIGNS FOR A MONSTRANCE

75. 276 × 186 mm. Black chalk, pen with brown ink. (5571)

76. 123 × 98 mm. Black chalk, pen with brown ink. (5577)

77. 103 × 65 mm. Black chalk, pen with brown ink. (5576)

Lit.: Brauer and Wittkower, p. 172 notes 3 and 4.

Free variations on Bernini's design for a monstrance recorded in a drawing at Ariccia (Brauer and Wittkower, Pl. 131a). The style is reminiscent of G. P. Schor.

78. DESIGN FOR A TABLE ORNAMENT   (1550)

288 × 196 mm. Black chalk.

From the Domenichino volumes.

The principal motives are two satyrs, one holding a goat, the other a monkey.

79. DESIGN FOR A TROPHY   (5569)

180 × 215 mm. Pen and brown ink.

Below two allegorical figures support a shield with a coronet and a cardinal's hat. Above is the double-headed, crowned Imperial Eagle. To the right a putto and a satyr.

80. STUDY FOR AN EQUESTRIAN MONUMENT   (5601)

482 × 323 mm. Pen and brown ink, with brown and blue wash.

The design shows a large mural monument based on Bernini's Constantine, with a general in wig and Roman armour on a rearing horse against a curtain. The figures are on a base with space for an inscription, a relief of a battle, and captive Orientals. The whole group is enclosed between two Ionic columns, supporting a broken pediment filled with weapons and a figure of Death over a blank coat of arms capped with a coronet of unidentifiable (but not Italian) type. The columns are decorated with a series of battle-reliefs which wind round them as on the Columns of Trajan and Marcus Aurelius. The prominence of Oriental captives suggests a connection with the defeat of the Turks in the battle of St. Gotthard in 1664, or the Siege of Vienna in 1683.

Fig. 8   Cat. No. 83

GIOVANNI BONATTI
(c. 1635–81)

So little is known of this artist that there is no means of checking the old attributions of the following drawings. The inscriptions seem, however, to date from the eighteenth century, and the style of the drawings is perfectly consistent with Bonatti's few known paintings, such as the *S. Carlo Borromeo* in the Uffizi. Other drawings in the same manner and with similar inscriptions are in the British Museum. See also above, No. 11.

81. LOT AND HIS DAUGHTERS   (6758)

196 × 268 mm. Red and white chalk.

Inscribed: *Gio. Bonatti.*

82. THE ADORATION OF THE SHEPHERDS   (6790)

195 × 279 mm. Black and white chalk on grey paper.

Inscribed: *Gio. Bonatti.*

83. THE VIRGIN AND CHILD APPEARING TO A FRANCISCAN MONK (*Fig. 8*)   (6819)

273 × 197 mm. Black and white chalk and grey wash on brown-grey paper. Inscribed: *Gio. Bonatti.*

To the left of the Madonna is the figure of a bishop holding a book; to the right that of a nun (?).

GIACINTO CALANDRUCCI
(1646–1707)

No drawings can be definitely attributed to Calandrucci on the basis of a connection with paintings by him, but there is a fairly large series of drawings attributed to him in the different Cabinets of Europe, which show a particular style consistent with the following drawings.

84. THE CORONATION OF THE VIRGIN   (6796)
284 × 232 mm. Pen and brown wash, heightened with white.
Apparently a study for the circular ceiling painting in the first chapel to the left in SS. Domenico e Sisto, Rome, the author of which is unfortunately not recorded in the Guides, but which is quite consistent with the style of Calandrucci. The composition has a general similarity to a painting of the same subject in the Pallavicini collection, attributed to Lazzaro Baldi (cf. F. Zeri, *La Galleria Pallavicini*, Florence, 1959, No.12).

85. THE MARTYRDOM OF ST. LAWRENCE   (4423)
170 × 262 mm. Pen and brown wash over black chalk.

86. THE VIRGIN AND CHILD APPEARING TO A BISHOP   (4421)
273 × 199 mm. Pen and brown wash over black chalk.
The last two drawings are from the volume containing works by Pietro de Pietri, Masucci and other followers of Maratta.

Fig. 9   Cat. No. 93

GIACINTO CALANDRUCCI (after)

87. THE HOLY FAMILY WITH ST. ANNE AND OTHER SAINTS   (6726)
530 × 323 mm. Red chalk.
Copy of the painting in S. Paolo alla Regola, Rome.

88. THREE HERMITS   (6725)
547 × 328 mm. Red chalk.
Copy of the painting in S. Maria in Traspontina, Rome.

89. THE VIRGIN AND CHILD APPEARING TO ST. PHILIP NERI   (6724)
537 × 327 mm. Red chalk.

90. THE VIRGIN AND CHILD ADORED BY ST. JOHN AND OTHER SAINTS   (6723)
535 × 363 mm. Red chalk.
The originals of the last two drawings have not been traced, but as they clearly form a series with Nos.87 and 88 they are probably also after Calandrucci. No.89 is based on Maratta's painting in the Uffizi (cf. No.262).

GIACINTO CALANDRUCCI
(attributed to)

91. THE ASSUMPTION   (4516)
417 × 295 mm. Pen and brown wash, heightened with white, on brown-tinted paper.
From the Cortona volumes.

92. THE ENTOMBMENT   (4152)
157 × 195 mm. Pen and brown wash over black chalk.
From the Maratta volumes.

ANDREA CAMASSEI
(1602–48/9)

93. THE PIETÀ (*Fig. 9*)   (4351)
395 × 289 mm. Red chalk, heightened with white.
Exact study for the painting in S. Maria della Concezione, Rome, probably executed between 1631 and 1636 and reproduced in Waterhouse, Fig. 9.

APOLLO

94. 359 × 230 mm. Black and white chalk on grey-green paper. (*Fig. 10*)   (4909)

95. 359 × 237 mm. Black and white chalk on grey-green paper.   (4960)
Lit.: A. Blunt, *Journal of the Warburg and Courtauld Institutes*, xxii, 1959, p. 287.
Studies for the ceiling painting of *Apollo and the Muses*, formerly in the Palazzo Barberini and known through the engraving in the *Aedes Barberinae*.

Fig. 10   Cat. No. 94

96. STUDY OF A NUDE MAN, SEATED, RIGHT LEG
RAISED, HOLDING A CRUTCH   (01216)
493×368 mm. Red chalk, heightened with white. Inscribed:
Camassei.

97. STUDY OF A NUDE MAN, SEATED, LEANING HIS
HEAD AND ARMS ON HIS RAISED RIGHT LEG   (01217)
544×406 mm. Red chalk, heightened with white. Inscribed
on mount: *Camassei.*

98. A MALE NUDE CROWNED WITH VINE-LEAVES (4902)
426×251 mm. Red chalk, with touches of white. Inscribed:
Andrea Camassei.

GIOVANNI ANGELO CANINI
(1617–66)

99. LANDSCAPE WITH HILLS AND HOUSES NEAR A
RIVER (*Fig. 11*)   (3542)
115×328 mm. Red chalk. Inscribed on mount: *Gio: Ang:
Canini.*

Since no paintings or drawings of landscapes seem to be
known by Canini, there is no means of checking the
attribution.

100. LANDSCAPE WITH A RUINED BUILDING ON A HILL
155×265 mm. Black chalk.   (5821)

101. LANDSCAPE WITH A BRIDGE AND A CASTLE (5822)
161×263 mm. Red chalk.

These two drawings, without a traditional attribution,
appear to be by the same hand as No.99.

102. A SHEET OF STUDIES   (3543)
178×222 mm. Pen and brown ink. Inscribed on mount:
Gio. Ang. Canini.
Studies of a woman's head, drapery, and a tree.

103. STUDY OF A MALE NUDE, STANDING, SEEN FROM
BELOW   (01228)
514×395 mm. Red chalk. Inscribed in ink (erased): *Angelus
Caninius Romanus . . . (?fecit)*, and in black chalk: *Angelo
Canini.*

Fig. 11   Cat. No. 99

104. STUDY OF A MALE NUDE, SEATED TO RIGHT, LEFT LEG AND ARM RAISED AND EXTENDED (01229)

396 × 476 mm. Red chalk. Inscribed in ink: *Io Angelus Caninius Romae Delint*.

105. STUDY OF A MALE NUDE PUSHING ON A POLE (4853)

438 × 290 mm. Red chalk. Inscribed: *Jo. Angelo Canini Del*.

ANGELO CAROSELLI (1585–1652)
(attributed to)

106. JUDITH AND HOLOFERNES (*Plate 1*) (5141)

215 × 337 mm. Pen and brown wash, heightened with body-colour, on dark grey paper.

This very unusual drawing seems from its general character and the treatment of light to be close to Saraceni and Caroselli. The heaviness of the forms suggests the latter rather than the former, and this attribution is supported by similarities to paintings ascribed with varying degrees of certainty to the artist. The general pattern is close, in reverse, to a painting of the same subject, which in 1927 belonged to the H. J. Brungs collection and was exhibited in that year at Wertheim's in Berlin. The head of the nurse recalls the painting of a *Young Woman singing beside an old one* (American private collection; reproduced Voss, p. 107), or even more closely the *Fortune-Teller*, formerly in the Gerini collection and known from an outline engraving in Rosini, *Storia della pittura italiana esposta coi monumenti*, 1852, vi, opp. p. 136. Since, however, no drawings by Caroselli are known, the attribution must be regarded as tentative. The technique is in some ways reminiscent of early drawings by Pietro da Cortona.

SERAFINO CESARETTI

Five small miniature paintings, heavily varnished, have been inserted by Sir William Drummond in his presentation copy of the *Odes of Horace*, given to King George IV in 1828.

Vol. I. Ode 15: HELEN AND PARIS ABOUT TO EMBARK. 104 × 208 mm. Within ornamental border. Inscribed on the page below: *Serafino Cesaretti pinxit Rome 1828*.

The design is taken from a classical gem.

Ode 15: HELEN AND PARIS UPBRAIDED BY NEREUS. 132 × 222 mm. Within ornamental border. Similarly inscribed below the drawing.

Vol. II. Ode 4: BRISEIS PRESENTED TO ACHILLES. 158 × 231 mm. Within ornamental border. Inscribed: *Serafino Cesaretti dipinse Roma 1828*.

Ode 4: A CLASSICAL HERO SLAYING A SHEEP. 135 × 115 mm. Oval, within ornamental border. Similarly inscribed, below the drawing.

Ode 14: HERCULES SLAYING GERYON. 135 × 115 mm. Oval, within ornamental border. Similarly inscribed, below the drawing.

See *Catalogue of English Drawings*, under Sir William Gell.

Fig. 12   Cat. No. 107

FABRIZIO CHIARI
(c.1615–95)

107. ALLEGORY IN HONOUR OF FERDINAND, KING OF HUNGARY (*Fig. 12*) (6821)

331 × 228 mm. Pen and brown ink, with black wash. Inscribed: *Fabrizio Chiari*.

Composition known from an engraving by C. Bloemaert, dated 1648, and dedicated to the King by Frederick Alexander Kotulin. Ferdinand was the son of the Emperor Ferdinand III, but predeceased him in 1654. The engraving differs in certain details from the drawing: in the latter the King is being crowned by a putto, whereas in the engraving he is shown wearing the crown of Hungary, while the putto flies towards him bearing another crown, presumably that of the Empire.

SEBASTIANO CONCA
(c.1680–1764)

108. HEAD OF AN ANGEL (5376)

290 × 220 mm. Red, black, blue and ochre chalk. Inscribed on mount: *del Conca*.

The angel is of a type that occurs frequently in Conca's paintings.

Fig. 13   Cat. No. 109

109. PORTRAIT OF A LADY WITH A DOG (*Fig. 13*) (0197)

256 × 180 mm. Pen and dark-brown ink, heightened with white, on brown paper. Signed: *Sebastiano Concha fece à Roma*.

SEBASTIANO CONCA (attributed to)

110. THE SUBMISSION OF AN ORIENTAL QUEEN TO A ROMAN GENERAL   (6817)

146 × 217 mm. Pen and dark-brown ink, heightened with white, on brown paper.

The attribution, which is tentative, is based on the similarity of this drawing to one at Holkham with an early attribution to Conca.

GUILLAUME COURTOIS
(called CORTESE or BORGOGNONE)
(1628–79)

One drawing by this artist, French by birth but Roman by adoption, was catalogued among the French drawings (Blunt, No.32), but since the publication of this volume of the catalogue others have been identified and are listed below.

111. THE SACRIFICE OF AARON (*Fig. 14*)   (6795)

362 × 278 mm. Black chalk, pen and bistre wash, heightened

with body-colour, on yellowish-brown paper. Damaged and mended at the edges.

Study for the painting by Courtois on the left wall of the chapel at the end of the right aisle in S. Marco, Rome.

GUILLAUME COURTOIS
(attributed to)

112. A PRIEST HOLDING TWO STAFFS   (0245)

389 × 233 mm. Red chalk on buff paper.

The attribution is based on the similarity of certain drawings by Courtois, reproduced by F. A. Salvagnini, *I Pittori Borgognini*, Rome, 1937, particularly the *St. Dominic* on Pl. 25.

113. A MONK CARRYING A BUNDLE   (0177)

247 × 188 mm. Pen and brown wash over red chalk.

The old mount apparently had an attribution to Guglielmo Cortese, and this is borne out by the style of the drawing.

114. THE HOLY FAMILY   (6783)

137 × 116 mm. Pen and brown wash over red chalk.

The attribution is purely tentative and is based on the general similarity in style to No.113. Another drawing in precisely the same style is in the Albertina (cf. *Zeichnungen der Toskanischen, Umbrischen und Römischen Schulen*, No.488) as 'Kreis des Caravaggio'.

Fig. 14   Cat. No. 111

Fig. 15   Cat. No. 116

JACQUES COURTOIS
(called CORTESE or BORGOGNONE)
(1621–75)

Four drawings attributed to this artist, who, like his brother, worked mainly in Rome, were catalogued in the volume dealing with the French School (Blunt, Nos. 33–36), but since the publication of that volume others have been identified and are listed below.

ST. LOUIS

115. 173 × 125 mm., including small later enlargements. Red chalk, pen and bistre wash.   (6349)

Inv. A, p. 127: Courtois.

116. 220 × 130 mm. Pen and bistre wash. Inscribed in an 18th-century hand: *S. Rosa*. (*Fig. 15*)   (6123)

Studies for the principal figure in Courtois' painting of *The Victory of St. Louis* in the Oratorio della Congregazione delle

Prima Primaria in the Collegio Romano, Rome (cf. F. A. Salvagnini, *I Pittori Borgognoni*, Rome, 1937, Pl. 44). The old attribution of No. 116 to Salvator Rosa is comprehensible since some of his early battle-pieces contain similar figures, which no doubt influenced Courtois. The present drawings are, however, closer to Courtois' painting, and the connection is established by the fleurs-de-lys which appear on the armour and on the trappings of the horse. In the painting the group appears in the opposite sense. Both drawings contain indications of the battle behind the figure of St. Louis.

117. A BATTLE (*Plate 44*)   (4523)

195 × 268 mm. Pen and brown wash.

Inv. A, p. 111, as Cortona. 'The Combatt of Aeneas and Turnus'.

This drawing is closely similar in style to Nos. 115 and 116. It may be related to one of the battle scenes in the Oratorio, but there is not enough evidence to establish the connection.

JACQUES COURTOIS (attributed to)
STUDIES OF HORSEMEN

118. 99 × 242 mm. Pen and brown ink. Numbered: *18* in top right-hand corner. (*Fig. 16*)   (0175)

119. 111 × 193 mm. Pen and brown ink.   (0179)

120. A CAVALRY SKIRMISH   (6336)

251 × 376 mm. Pen and brown wash on darkened white paper. Inscribed: *Borgognone*.

121. ST. MARTIN AND THE BEGGAR, ST. JAMES, AND A BISHOP   (5998)

184 × 122 mm. Pen and brown wash. Squared. Perhaps for an engraving.

The *St. James* is copied from Marcantonio's engraving after Raphael (Bartsch, xiv, p. 75, No.67).

JACQUES COURTOIS (follower of)

122. A HORSEMAN GALLOPING OUT OF A WALLED CITY   (6348)

163 × 254 mm. Pen and bistre, with some black chalk.
Inv. A, p. 127: Courtois.

123. HORSEMEN OUTSIDE A WALLED CITY   (6345)

128 × 198 mm. Pen and brown ink, with brown and grey wash.

Fig. 16   Cat. No. 118

Fig. 17   Cat. No. 124

CIRO FERRI
(1628–89)

Ferri was one of the most competent followers of Pietro da Cortona and his drawings, particularly those in black chalk, are often difficult to distinguish from his master's. The group at Windsor, though not extensive, contains several firm starting points for the analysis of his style. No.124, a study for the dome of S. Agnese, gives an idea of his rather loose handling of pen and wash; the *St. Paul at Athens* (No.126), engraved in his lifetime, shows his use of a more complex technique; *Moses striking the Rock* (No.125), also engraved, is an example of his most finished black chalk drawing. In the same manner are two large drawings (Nos.130 and 131) illustrating the life of Urban VIII, which can be ascribed to him on strong circumstantial evidence. Two other designs with very early inscriptions show him working on his large scale schemes. One (No.129) is for a purely architectural work, with which his name is connected by the documents; the other (Nos.127–8), for a fresco decoration, is not otherwise certified, but the style of the drawing entirely confirms the old inscription. On the basis of these relatively certain drawings four others at Windsor have been attributed to him with a reasonable degree of confidence; but the ascription must be regarded as tentative, since the various hands working in the studio of Cortona are still hard to distinguish.

124. A GROUP OF SAINTS ON CLOUDS (*Fig. 17*)   (4518)

189 × 264 mm. Pen and brown wash over black chalk.

Verso: Four figures, one crowned, hovering on a cloud over a river.

From the Cortona volumes.

Study for the fresco in the dome of S. Agnese a Piazza Navona, Rome, begun in 1670, left unfinished at the artist's death (cf. Waterhouse, p. 63), and engraved by Michel Dorigny. The figures of St. Peter and St. John the Baptist at his feet appear exactly in the fresco, but the others have been changed.

The drawings from which Dorigny's engravings were made are in the Palazzo Silva at Domodossola (cf. B. C. Chiovenda, 'Ciro Ferri, G. B. Gaulli e la cupola della chiesa di S. Agnese in Piazza Navona', *Commentari*, x, 1959, p. 19, and Pl. vi).

125. MOSES STRIKING THE ROCK (*Plate 43*)   (01117)

374 × 706 mm. Black chalk, gone over in some places with the stylus.

Exact preparation for the engraving by Pietro Aquila inscribed: *Cyrus Ferrus Inventor et Delineavit*, and dedicated to Cardinal Jacopo Ninio.

126. ST. PAUL AT ATHENS (*Fig. 18*)   (4487)

319 × 220 mm. Black chalk with pale brown wash, heightened with white.

From the volume of Cortona, Ferri, etc.

Exh.: Fitzwilliam Museum, Cambridge, 1959, No.30, as Cortona.

Corresponds exactly, in reverse, to the engraving by C. Bloemaert, dated 1679.

PERSEUS BEING ARMED BY JUPITER AND MINERVA

127. 519 × 732 mm. Black and red chalk. Pressed through with a stylus. Inscribed: *di Ciro Ferri.* (*Fig. 19*)   (6835)

128. 521 × 722 mm. Black and red chalk. Pressed through with a stylus. Inscribed: *di Ciro Ferri.* (*Fig. 20*)   (6836)

Fig. 18   Cat. No. 126

Fig. 19

Cat. No. 127

Fig. 20

Cat. No. 128

The two drawings form the upper and lower half of a single design. In the upper panel Jupiter, seated on a cloud, sends his eagle to carry a sword to his son, Perseus, who stands in armour below. To the right of Jupiter, on another cloud, is Minerva, who addresses Vulcan at his forge below. In the background Andromeda is tied to a rock on the left, while her family mourn on the right. At the top of the frame are two trophies, one of classical, one of Turkish armour, and below are two captives, one a Turk and one a Trojan. The exact relevance of the Turkish captive to the story of Perseus is not clear, but the drawing is probably an allegory in honour of one of the victories over the Turks, perhaps the battle of Lepanto.

129. DESIGN FOR THE HIGH ALTAR OF S. GIOVANNI DEI FIORENTINI (01115)

893 × 378 mm. Pen and bistre wash over black chalk. Inscribed: *Disegno fatto da Ciro Ferri per l'Altar Maggiore di S. Gio. de Fiorentini fatto poi dal Borromino come presentemente si vede quale è della Casa Falconieri*. A scale at the side.

Elevation and plan of the whole altar wall. A sculptured relief of the *Baptism of Christ* under a curved pediment supported by Corinthian columns, with the Holy Ghost in the tympanum. In the attic above God the Father hovers over the scene.

The High Altar of S. Giovanni dei Fiorentini was begun by Pietro da Cortona in the late 1630's and, after a long interruption, continued by Borromini from 1664 until his death in 1667, after which it was completed by Ciro Ferri (cf. E. Hempel, *Francesco Borromini*, Vienna, 1924, p. 189).

Ferri's drawing shows the whole east wall of the choir, but the design differs in almost every respect from the altar as it stands today, and as it is shown in the engraving in Giacomo di Rossi, *Disegni di vari altari e cappelle*, 1713, Pl. 15, which varies in small details of decoration from the original. Ferri's drawing shows a broad, heavy frontispiece, with two pairs of coupled Corinthian columns and a curved pediment, of which the central part is set back. Behind the coupled columns are two single columns, behind which again two half-columns flank what appears to be a relief of the *Baptism*. The plan shows two variants for this part of the design. In the field of the pediment is the Holy Ghost in an oval, probably intended for painted glass. Above the main part of the altar, in the attic, is a panel with the figure of God the Father, and above it two putti carrying the Cross, which stands out against a plain window.

This design is, from the ground upwards, inconsistent with what exists today in the church. It might, therefore, be a design by Ferri made in competition with his master Cortona when the altar was first planned, but the date of Ferri's birth makes this impossible. One can only suppose, therefore, that Ferri made the drawing at a later stage in the hope that whatever had been built would be taken down, and that he would be allowed a free hand. This is consistent with what is recorded of his behaviour over the decoration of the church of S. Agnese, where, alarmed at the success of Gaulli's pendentive paintings and asserting that they would clash with his dome, he proposed to destroy them, although they had only been executed a few years, and replace them with other frescoes by himself (cf. Chiovenda, *op. cit.*, p. 17).

The drawing was most probably made when Ferri took over work on the altar after Borromini's death in 1667, but it is possible that he might have made the design in competition with Borromini in 1664.

The drawing is unusual in its size and the elaboration of detail. It gives a clear idea of Ferri's style of architectural drawing and of the way in which he interpreted the principles of his master Cortona.

130. URBAN VIII INVOKING THE PROTECTION OF ST. PETER AND ST. PAUL (*Fig. 22*) (4507)

350 × 480 mm. Black chalk.

Study for a painting on paper in a room on the north front of the Palazzo Barberini, probably intended as a cartoon for tapestry and later used as a wall decoration. The cartoon is in the opposite sense, but a smaller oil version in the Galleria Nazionale, Rome, is in the same sense as the drawing. In certain details, however, the cartoon follows the drawing more closely than does the small oil version. Cf. *Fig. 21*.

131. URBAN VIII INSPECTING THE PLANS FOR THE FORTIFICATION OF CASTELFRANCO (OR MANTUA)

374 × 452 mm. Black chalk. (*Fig. 23*) (4506)

Study, in the same sense, for a painting on paper in the same room of the Palazzo Barberini (*Fig. 21*; cf. *Bollettino d'Arte*, xxxvi, 1951, p. 376). In this article the painting is said to refer to Mantua, but in the exhibition catalogue quoted below the city is said to be Castelfranco.

The attribution of these drawings presents certain difficulties. The cartoons have often been ascribed to Pietro da Cortona, but Don Urbano Barberini in his article on the Arazzeria Barberini (*Bollettino d'Arte*, xxxv, 1950, p. 151) states categorically, on the basis of documents, that the artist had no part in designing them, and that they were made after 1647, the last year of his work for the factory. The name of Romanelli has also been proposed, *e.g.* by H. Goebel (*Die Wandteppiche . . . in Frankreich, Italien, Spanien und Portugal*, Leipzig, 1928, pp. 420 ff., and *Der Cicerone*, xxi, 1929, p. 305), and is accepted by Hess (*Passeri*, p. 309). On the other hand, there are three drawings in the Gabinetto Nazionale delle Stampe, Rome (Nos. 124386, 124459, 124471), directly connected with No. 131, one of which is inscribed on the *verso: Jo Ciro Ferri 1683*. These drawings were shown in the exhibition of *Cortoneschi a Roma*, held in the Palazzo Barberini in 1956 (Nos. 23–25), and on the evidence of the inscription and also of style the author of the catalogue, Prof. Lidia Bianchi, attributed the cartoons to Ferri. This attribution would be supported by the Windsor drawings, which are like Ferri's finished black chalk drawings. The cartoons themselves are less like Ferri's work, but if the date of 1683 is correct, both Cortona and Romanelli are ruled out, since they died in the 1660's. The date is in itself curious, since after the death of Cardinal Francesco Barberini in 1679 the Arazzeria went into a decline, though it continued to produce tapestries.

It seems impossible, however, to escape the conclusion that the cartoons and the drawings were made by Ferri in about 1683. This would be a striking example of the degree to which he had lagged behind artistic developments in Rome and would provide a close parallel with the story of the dome of S. Agnese (cf. Chiovenda, *op. cit.*, p. 17).

Fig. 21   Room in the Palazzo Barberin

Fig. 22   Cat. No. 130   Fig. 23   Cat. No. 131

132. DAVID AND ABIGAIL   (4532)   133. ELIJAH AND THE WIDOW OF ZAREPHATH (?)
300 × 460 mm. Black chalk. Squared.   218 × 357 mm. Black chalk.   (4501)
From the Cortona volumes.   From the volume of Cortona, Ferri, etc.

Fig. 24   Cat. No. 140

A woman kneels beside a jar, holding a small bowl, while two children approach her, one pointing to a jar on the ground, the other carrying a waterpot. In the background, leaning on a wall, is a bearded man praying. Apart from the presence of the second boy, this composition would fit the story of Elijah and the widow.

134. THE VESTAL VIRGIN CLAUDIA   (4534)
225 × 196 mm. Black chalk.
From the Cortona volumes.

135. ERMINIA AND THE SHEPHERDS   (4352)
246 × 314 mm. Black chalk.
From the Maratta volumes.
Both these drawings are in the black chalk style which appears to be typical of Ferri.

CIRO FERRI (attributed to)

136. AN ANGEL AND A PUTTO SUPPORTING DRAPERY
                                                (6753)
228 × 167 mm. Red chalk, heightened with white, on grey-green paper.
The forms are Cortonesque, but somewhat heavy for him. In technique and handling this drawing is very close to a *Crucifixion* from the Malcolm collection in the British Museum (1895-9-15-665), which has been attributed to Ferri by von Below (*Beiträge zur Kenntnis Pietro da Cortonas*, Murnau, 1932, p. 101) on the basis of an engraving by Bloemaert.
For a copy after Ferri by Spierre, see Blunt, *French Drawings*, No. 300.

LUIGI GARZI
(1638-1721)

137. ST. CATHERINE RECEIVED INTO HEAVEN (*Plate 47*)
                                                (6824)
506 × 218 mm. Pen and brown wash. Inscribed: *di Garzi*.
A study, differing only in small details from the fresco on the ceiling of S. Caterina a Magnanapoli, Rome, a late work by Garzi (cf. Waterhouse, p. 64). Another study is in the Louvre (No. 9790). This drawing is in a highly personal abbreviated style, which can be readily identified in the following five pen drawings, some of which have old attributions to Garzi.

138. ALLEGORY OF FAITH   (6825)
397 × 201 mm. Pen and brown wash on brown-tinted paper. Inscribed: *di Garzi*.
Faith seated on clouds; below her Justice and Fortitude; above Fame with a trumpet.

MUTIUS SCAEVOLA
139. 150 × 330 mm. Black chalk, pen and brown ink, and water-colour. Inscribed: *di Garzi*.   (6719)

140. 129 × 255 mm. Pen and brown ink, with black wash. Squared. (*Fig. 24*)   (5552)
No. 140 is from the Bernini volumes.
The two compositions are connected in their principal groups; No. 139 has an old attribution to Garzi, and No. 140 is in his characteristic style.

141. THE CRUCIFIXION   (1803)
167 × 124 mm. Pen and brown wash over black chalk.
From the Carracci volumes, but clearly in the pen style of Garzi.

142. THE FLIGHT INTO EGYPT   (5671)
219 × 162 mm. Pen and brown wash over black chalk.
From the Lanfranco volumes.
The resemblance to No. 137 is not quite as close as in the above four cases, but the drawing seems to be by the same hand.

143. AN ALLEGORY OF PLENTY   (6826)
210 × 403 mm. Black and white chalk on blue paper. Inscribed: *L. Garzi*.
Plenty, seated on a cloud, is crowned by Fame. To the right, on another cloud, sits a youth wearing a crown and holding a sceptre.
The inscription, which is in the hand that appears on the pen drawings, carries conviction, since the chalk style of this and the two following drawings has the same economy as Garzi's manner and shows some of the same mannerisms.

Fig. 25   Cat. No. 145

144. THE VISION OF ST. FRANCIS   (6827)

393 × 258 mm. Black and white chalk on grey-brown paper. Inscribed: *Di Garzi.*

145. THE AGONY IN THE GARDEN (*Fig. 25*)   (6812)

266 × 359 mm. Black and white chalk on blue-grey paper. Inscribed: *Luigi Garzi.*

GIOVANNI BATTISTA GAULLI
(called BACICCIO)
(1639–1709)

Gaulli's drawings have been studied in an important article by M. V. Brugnoli ('Inediti del Gaulli', *Paragone*, vii, 1956, No.81, pp. 21 ff.). The authoress identifies eight of those at Windsor as studies for works known in the original or from engravings. Two portraits of Clement X and Innocent XI had already been attributed to Gaulli by Brauer and Wittkower. On the basis of this series the editors have tentatively ascribed to the artist several further drawings, most of which come, like those discussed by Brugnoli, from the Bernini or Cortona volumes, although a few come from the Maratta series. In addition they have classified as by followers others which seem to reflect Gaulli's mixture of Berninesque and Cortonesque elements, but which are not close enough to his manner to be given either to him or to his studio.

1. Drawings connected with known works

ROME, S. Agnese
ALLEGORY OF JUSTICE

Fresco in pendentive, executed between 1668 and 1671.

146. STUDY FOR THE WHOLE COMPOSITION (*Plate 48*)
                                                  (5550)

229 × 196 mm. Pen and brown ink, brown wash, over black chalk indications.

From the Bernini volumes.

Lit.: M. V. Brugnoli, *op. cit.*, p. 22, Fig. 15a.

Studies for the other pendentives are at Besançon.

ROME, S. Margherita
THE IMMACULATE CONCEPTION WITH ST. FRANCIS AND ST. CLARE

The painting was probably executed after 1680 and certainly before 1686 (cf. M. V. Brugnoli, *op. cit.*, p.30).

147. DRAWING FOR THE WHOLE COMPOSITION (4492)

299 × 187 mm. Pen, brown wash, heightened with white over black chalk. Squared.

Inv. A, p. 113: P. Cortona, Ciro Ferri, etc.

Lit.: M. V. Brugnoli, *op. cit.*, p. 30, Fig. 22a.

Agrees almost exactly with the painting itself.

ROME, S. Marta

The church was decorated by Gaulli and Fontana with paintings and stuccos soon after 1670 (cf. M. V. Brugnoli, *op. cit.*, p. 24).

148. STUDY FOR THE ALTAR   (5600)

346 × 261 mm. Pen and brown ink over black chalk, partly squared in chalk. Inscribed in chalk at foot: *Bernino.*

From the Bernini volumes.

Lit.: M. V. Brugnoli, *loc. cit.*, and Fig. 18a.

The connection with S. Marta, proposed by Brugnoli, is hypothetical but convincing.

ROME, Private Collection
THE SACRIFICE OF NOAH

The painting was published by Robert Enggass (*Paragone*, vii, 1956, p. 31, No.63), and discussed by M. V. Brugnoli, *op. cit.*, pp. 25 f.). Enggass published a second version of the design belonging to the Kress Foundation, with many features in common with the Roman version, but upright in format. He dates both versions to c.1690, but Brugnoli believes that the Roman painting is much earlier, c.1670.

The painting is based ultimately on a composition by Poussin from the Corsini collection, now at Tatton Hall, Cheshire, and engraved by Frey (repr. Blunt, 'La première période romaine de Poussin', *Actes du Colloque Poussin*, Paris, 1960, I, Figs. 133, 134). The design was also used by Castiglione (cf. A. Blunt, *The Drawings of G. B. Castiglione and Stefano della Bella at Windsor Castle*, London, 1954, p. 39, No.163, and A. Blunt, *Journal of the Warburg and Courtauld Institutes*, iii, 1939–40, p. 143, note 3), who gave it a much more Baroque form. It is likely that Gaulli knew both Poussin's and Castiglione's versions of the theme.

149. STUDY OF THE WHOLE COMPOSITION (*Plate 49*)
                                                  (5547)

270 × 350 mm. Pen, grey wash over black chalk, heightened with white, on brown paper.

From the Bernini volumes.

Lit.: M. V. Brugnoli, *loc. cit.*, and Fig. 17b.

The drawing differs substantially from both paintings in having God the Father supported by putti appearing to Noah and his family. Gaulli must have taken this group from the Poussin and Castiglione versions of the subject.

VIENNA, Czernin Collection
HOLY FAMILY WITH ST. ELIZABETH AND ST. JOHN

The painting, probably a *bozzetto*, was published by R. Enggass in the *Art Quarterly*, 1957, p. 11, Fig. 3.

150. STUDY FOR THE WHOLE COMPOSITION   (5554)

208 × 138 mm. Pen and black ink, grey wash, over some black chalk. Squared in black chalk.

From the Bernini volumes.

Lit.: M. V. Brugnoli, *op. cit.*, p. 31 note 1.

This drawing agrees almost exactly with the painted version. A drawing for the St. John is in Berlin.

Fig. 26   Cat. No. 152

154. AN ALLEGORY   (6789)

228 × 115 mm. Pen and brown ink, with black wash. Inscribed above: *NEC DUÆ NEC UNA*, and below: *Baciccio*.

Lit.: M. V. Brugnoli, *op. cit.*, p. 31 note 1.

To the right a girl, winged and wearing a crown, kneels and holds an open casket. She stretches out her right hand towards an old man who sits on the left, holding a flower. Between the two figures is an eagle, and above flies a putto pointing to the clipped trees of the garden.

Probably an allegory on gardening.

155. VENUS AND ADONIS (*Plate 50*)   (6761)

231 × 168 mm. Pen and dark brown ink, grey wash. Inscribed in pen at foot: *Baciccia*.

Inv. A, p. 128: 30 of Bacicia Galli, Lazaro Baldi, Baglione, &c.

Lit.: M. V. Brugnoli, *op. cit.*, p. 29.

The figure group is directly based on the painting of the subject by Rubens in The Hague.

156. PORTRAIT OF INNOCENT XI   (5531)

373 × 246 mm. Red and black chalk, some red wash, heightened with white.

Loose in the Bernini volumes, not traceable in Inv. A.

Lit.: Brauer and Wittkower, p. 157.

151. PORTRAIT OF VITALE GIORDANO OF BITONTO

Engraving after Gaulli, signed: *Benedict. Farjat*, an artist apparently unrecorded.

232 × 207 mm. Black chalk, rubbed, heightened with white, on white paper. Inscribed: *VITALIS IORDANUS BITONTINVS AETATIS A [NNORU] M LX. Io. Bap : Gaulli del.* in ornamental cartouche at foot of the oval surround. (5545)

From the Bernini volumes.

Lit.: M. V. Brugnoli, *op. cit.*, p. 32, note 1.

152. PORTRAIT OF DUILIUS (*Fig. 26*)   (5544)

331 × 233 mm. Black chalk, slight wash, heightened with white, on buff paper.

From the Bernini volumes.

Lit.: M. V. Brugnoli, *op. cit.*, p. 32, note 1.

Head and shoulders, nearly full face, in oval surround decorated with scrolls, coronet and blank shield; cartouche with inscription at foot.

2. *Drawings not connected with known works*

153. JOSEPH AND HIS BRETHREN   (5548)

225 × 319 mm. Pen with brown ink and black wash, on brown-tinted paper. Squared.

From the Bernini volumes.

Lit.: M. V. Brugnoli, *op. cit.*, p. 31 note 1.

Fig. 27   Cat. No. 159

Fig. 28   Cat. No. 161

This drawing was attributed on style to Gaulli by Brauer and Wittkower, together with another similar portrait of Alexander VIII in the Pierpont Morgan Library (repr. in *J. Pierpont Morgan Collection of Drawings*, London, 1912, iv, Pl. 175, as Bernini).

157. PORTRAIT OF CLEMENT X   (5533)
198 × 146 mm. Red and black chalk, on buff paper.
Lit.: Brauer and Wittkower, p. 157, note 2.
Loose in the Bernini volumes, not traceable in Inv. A.

GIOVANNI BATTISTA GAULLI
(attributed to)

158. THE ADORATION OF THE SHEPHERDS   (0258)
247 × 355 mm. Brown pen and wash. Squared.
Inv. A, p. 146: Gaulli.
A drawing strongly influenced by Castiglione, and therefore, if by Gaulli, probably an early work executed before or soon

after he left Genoa for Rome. The attribution of this and the following drawings is highly tentative, but they seem to be closer in style to Gaulli than to any other artist.

159. THE HOLY TRINITY WITH THE SYMBOLS OF THE PASSION (*Fig. 27*)   (6822)
508 × 397 mm. Pen and grey wash over red chalk. Inscribed: *Baciccia*.

160. TWO ALLEGORICAL FIGURES   (4525)
195 × 233 mm. Pen and brown wash over black chalk.
From the Cortona volumes.
Two flying figures, one wearing a crown and carrying a sceptre, the other carrying a second sceptre. The similarity of the crown to one appearing on a drawing by Carlo Fontana for the tomb of Queen Christina of Sweden (No.9903) suggests that this drawing may allude to this Queen.
Not mentioned by Brugnoli, who perhaps did not see the drawing, which has hitherto been classified as by Pietro da Cortona. The style is, however, much closer to Gaulli.

161. DESIGN FOR THE CEILING OF A CHURCH (*Fig. 28*)
(5563)

367 × 480 mm. Pen and brown wash over red chalk.

From the Bernini volumes.

In the central field a male Saint is received into Heaven.

162. TWO ALLEGORICAL FIGURES BELOW AN OVAL FRAME   (5616)

316 × 221 mm. Pen and brown wash over black chalk.

Verso: Two putti. Black chalk.

From the Bernini volumes.

Perhaps a design for a tomb with a relief-bust in the oval.

163. AN IMAGE OF THE VIRGIN AND CHILD CARRIED BY ANGELS   (4148)

241 × 184 mm. Pen and brown wash over black chalk.

From the Maratta volumes, but very close in style to No. 162.

164. See No. 20.

165. DESIGN FOR THE TOMB OF A CHILD   (5568)

266 × 188 mm. Pen and brown wash over black chalk. Two scales at the bottom.

From the Bernini volumes.

The child lies on a sarcophagus under a canopy at the top of which putti hold a crown over him.

The drawing of the architecture is very close to No. 148 in its shaky line, and the figures recall No. 160 and other drawings tentatively ascribed to Gaulli.

GIOVANNI BATTISTA GAULLI
(follower of)

166. A BISHOP CARRIED UP TO HEAVEN   (5549)

360 × 248 mm. Pen and brown wash over red chalk, heightened with white and grey gouache.

From the Bernini volumes.

167. ALLEGORY OF THE OLD AND NEW DISPENSATIONS   (4179)

299 × 209 mm. Pen and brown wash, heightened with white.

From the Maratta volumes.

The four Evangelists occupy the foreground, while at the back on the right Melchizedek stands beside an altar, offering up the Shewbread. Above flies an angel holding what appear to be the Tablets of the Law.

168. ST. PETER AND ST. PAUL   (6746)

166 × 164 mm. The composition enclosed in a circle. Pen and brown ink, with black wash over black chalk. Inscribed: *Baccicia.*

In spite of the inscription the drawing is too feeble to be by Gaulli.

169. THE CHRIST CHILD APPEARING TO ST. ANTHONY OF PADUA   (5516)

266 × 180 mm. Pen and brown wash.

ANTONIO GHERARDI
(1644–1702)

Three drawings (Nos. 170–172) can be attributed to Antonio Gherardi for two reasons. Stylistically they combine a Venetian mode of composition and *di sotto in sù* perspective in the manner of Veronese with a Roman style in drawing—a combination hard to be found in any Seicento works apart from those of Gherardi; and further, one of them, No. 170, is related to one of Gherardi's paintings on the ceiling of S. Maria in Trivio in Rome. Since they all represent Old Testament themes and are planned on a consistent perspective view, they were probably designed for a ceiling similar to that of S. Maria in Trivio. Three other drawings (Nos. 173–175) can be added to this group and ascribed to Gherardi on grounds of style.

A painting of the *Death of Dido* from the County Museum, Los Angeles, shown in the Seicento exhibition in Venice in 1959 (No. 159), is very close to these drawings in its general method of composition.

170. ESTHER BEFORE AHASUERUS (*Fig. 29*)   (6708)

275 × 245 mm. Pen and brown ink with black wash.

Based on Veronese's *Esther* in S. Sebastiano, Venice, and close in many details, particularly the architecture and figures in the upper right-hand corner, to Gherardi's *Presentation of the Virgin* on the ceiling of S. Maria in Trivio, Rome (repr. A. Mezzetti, 'La Pittura di Antonio Gherardi', *Bollettino d'Arte*, 1948, p. 168).

Fig. 29   Cat. No. 170

Fig. 30   Cat. No. 176

171. THE TRIUMPH OF DAVID (6709)

397 × 271 mm. Oval. Pen and brown ink, with black wash over black chalk.

172. THE PRESENTATION IN THE TEMPLE (6707)

240 × 413 mm. Black wash over black chalk.

Nos. 171 and 172 probably form a series with No. 170.

173. THE JUDGMENT OF SOLOMON (6706)

397 × 271 mm. Oval. Pen and brown ink, with black wash over black chalk. Squared.

174. SOLOMON SACRIFICING TO IDOLS (6793)

238 × 368 mm. Black wash over black chalk.

175. THE BURIAL OF ST. MARK (6705)

297 × 317 mm. Black wash over black chalk.

The body of the Saint is carried up a flight of steps to a tomb.

PIER LEONE GHEZZI
(1674–1755)

176. PORTRAIT OF HIS FATHER, GIUSEPPE GHEZZI

(Fig. 30)   (097)

359 × 261 mm. Pen and brown wash, heightened with white over black chalk, on brown-tinted paper. Inscribed on the *verso: Ritratto del Giuseppe Ghezzi di eta di* Anni 84. *Fatto da me Cav. Ghezzi suo figliolo 1721.*

This inscription conflicts with the generally accepted date of 1634 for Giuseppe Ghezzi's birth.

177. STUDY FOR THE HEAD OF GOD THE FATHER (5360)

362 × 265 mm. Red chalk. Inscribed in Pier Leone Ghezzi's hand: *Il P. eterno dio dipinto dal Giuseppe Ghezzi nella chiesa nostra di Roma et io Cav^re. Ghezzi lo disegnai di mia memoria.*

The phrase 'la chiesa nostra' should refer to the Marchigian church of S. Salvatore in Lauro, Rome, which was restored by Giuseppe Ghezzi and for which he painted a *Pietà*. This does not, however, contain a figure of God the Father, and Pier Leone Ghezzi, who admits that he made the drawing from memory, must have been mistaken in thinking that it was after this work. The head is in fact very like that of God the Father in Cortona's altarpiece of *The Holy Trinity* in St. Peter's.

GIACINTO GIMIGNANI
(1611–81)

178. THE ADORATION OF THE SHEPHERDS (*Fig. 31*)

(4539)

277 × 198 mm. Pen and brown wash, on brown-tinted paper. From the Cortona volumes.

Fig. 31   Cat. No. 178

Fig. 32   Cat. No. 179

The attribution to Gimignani is based on the similarity of the types of Gimignani's *Adoration of the Kings* in the chapel of the Propaganda Fide, painted in 1634 (repr. Waterhouse, Pl. 29).

179. THE FINDING OF ROMULUS AND REMUS (*Fig. 32*) (6714)

107 × 420 mm. Pen and brown wash, with blue and white gouache, on brown-tinted paper. The right-hand end of the composition is cut off. Inscribed: *del Gimignani*.

Study for the frieze in the Palazzo Pamphili, Piazza Navona, Rome, attributed to Gimignani by E. K. Waterhouse, p. 71.

LODOVICO GIMIGNANI
(1643–97)

180. THE FAMILY OF DARIUS BEFORE ALEXANDER (6715)

345 × 491 mm. Pen and brown wash, heightened with white over red chalk.

Inv. A, p. 128: Gimignani.

181. THE CONTINENCE OF SCIPIO (?) (6716)

345 × 488 mm. Pen and brown wash, heightened with white over black chalk.

Fig. 33   Cat. No. 182

Inv. A, p. 128: Gimignani.

The prominent part played in the scene by a bearded old man makes the identification of the subject with the story of Scipio uncertain, but he also appears in a painting which clearly represents this subject, attributed to Gaulli, at Nîmes, which Gimignani seems to have known.

182. MARCUS CURIUS DENTATUS REJECTING THE GIFTS OF THE SAMNITE AMBASSADORS (*Fig. 33*)   (6808)

253 × 387 mm. Black wash, heightened with white over black chalk. Inscribed: *L. Gimignani*.

183. MERCURY ORDERING AENEAS TO LEAVE CARTHAGE   (5546)

300 × 505 mm. Pen and brown wash, heightened with white, on prepared paper, washed with brown colour.

From the Bernini volumes.

A drawing of the right-hand half of the composition is in the Schiff (formerly Cogswell) collection (*Catalogue*, New York, 1915, Pl. xi). This is there attributed, for no obvious reason, to Gabbiani. The Schiff drawing has in the left foreground a large coat of arms, which unfortunately cannot be identified.

These four drawings are clearly by the same hand; three of them have old attributions to Gimignani, and all are close in style to the drawing in Berlin for his fresco in S. Silvestro in Capite, Rome.

GIOVANNI LANFRANCO
(1582–1647)

The problem of Lanfranco's drawings has hitherto been little examined, and few have been identified as preparations for certain works. The Windsor series is, therefore, of great importance, since it contains thirty-four that can be connected with surviving paintings and two more with engravings. Many of the paintings can be dated at least approximately, and the series of drawings therefore provides a basis for studying the development of his style in this field.

Apart from the enigmatic *Transfiguration*, which would never have been accepted as by Lanfranco at all but for the fact that it is engraved, and which must, owing to its Mannerist elements, date from his youth, the earliest drawings in the Windsor series show above all traces of his training in the studio of the Carracci, whether it be in the kneeling figure of *St. Andrew adoring the Cross* (No. 185) of c.1607, or in the *ignudi* for the Sala dei Corazzieri in the Quirinal of c.1611–12. The date of the *Pentecost* at Fermo cannot be determined more precisely than within a bracket of fifteen years, 1615–30, and nothing is known in Lanfranco's work like the drawing for it (No.186). It was traditionally ascribed to Maratta, not entirely without reason, because the free, almost loose style of drawing suggests the end rather than the beginning of the seventeenth century; and yet its connection with the painting seems to be undeniable. The

group of drawings related to the frescoes in St. Peter's, executed between 1629 and 1632, is marked by a distinctive style and technique. The constant use of sharp foreshortening is in part due to the height at which the frescoes are to be seen, but it is also a sign of Lanfranco's evolution towards the Baroque, which had been manifested in the dome of S. Andrea della Valle of the immediately preceding years. These drawings are all on a rough, light grey-brown paper and in a vigorous style, somewhat schematic in its treatment of anatomy, but they are among the most lively of the artist's studies. The Royal Collection is peculiarly rich in drawings of Lanfranco's Neapolitan period, and the series must constitute the remains of a sketchbook which he used during the whole of his years in the city. Many of the drawings can be directly connected with frescoes in SS. Apostoli or in S. Martino, and in some cases the figures in the two churches repeat each other so closely that it is difficult to be certain with which to connect a particular study. Compared with the studies for St. Peter's the Neapolitan drawings are freer and more rapid. Unhappily they are usually on coloured paper and in a rather faint chalk, so that their qualities do not appear well in reproduction. The few pen and wash drawings for the SS. Apostoli, though perhaps coarser in quality, lose less of their character in reproduction.

Almost all the following drawings come from a single series which is attributed to Lanfranco in Inventory A, which no doubt merely records a long and respectable tradition. A few come from the volumes devoted to the Carracci or to Domenichino, and one or two others from miscellaneous volumes, which are specified in each entry. There is some reason to suppose that the main series belonged to Carlo Maratta. Most of his collection passed to the Albani and so to the Royal Collection, and in one instance we can trace what appears to be a direct borrowing by Maratta from a drawing by Lanfranco (No. 197). It is, of course, possible that he may have known the fresco in Naples for which it is a study, but on the whole it seems more likely that he turned to his own collection for inspiration in this instance.

1. Drawings connected with known works

AUGSBURG, Museum
THE ASSUMPTION

Painted for the Fugger family in 1631 (cf. Voss, p. 527; reproduced in *Commentari*, ix, 1958, Pl. xxvi, Fig. 13).

184. STUDY FOR THE UPPER PART OF THE COMPOSITION   (4350)

218 × 180 mm. Pen and brown ink, grey and brown wash, heightened with white over black chalk.

From the Maratta volumes.

The very free sketch differs in many ways from the painting, but is probably a first preparation for it.

Fig. 34   Cat. No. 186 *recto*

BERLIN, Kaiser-Friedrich-Museum
ST. ANDREW ADORING THE CROSS

Reproduced in Voss, p. 224. Probably c.1607 (*ibid.*, p.524).

185. STUDY FOR ST. ANDREW   (5704)

402 × 258 mm. Black and white chalk on grey-green paper.

Verso: Studies of drapery, a hand and a foot.

FERMO, S. Filippo
PENTECOST

The painting, executed between 1615 and 1630, is discussed in *Paragone*, iii, No.29, p. 19, and reproduced Fig. 10.

186. STUDIES FOR THE WHOLE COMPOSITION (*Fig. 34*)
                                              (4177)

316 × 189 mm. Black chalk.

From the Maratta volumes.

The *recto* and *verso* each show a complete study in rough but vigorous chalk strokes. In the *recto* version the main features of the design agree with the painting, but on the *verso* the whole scene is planned more asymmetrically on a more Baroque pattern.

Another drawing for the painting is in the Uffizi (cf. *Paragone, loc. cit.*).

LENINGRAD, Hermitage
THE ANNUNCIATION

187. STUDIES FOR THE VIRGIN ANNUNCIATE   (5709)

237 × 339 mm. Black chalk, touches of white, on dark grey paper.

Verso: Studies of an arm and drapery.

The *recto* shows two studies for the upper part of the body and one of the head of the Virgin.

The date of the painting is not known, but it was probably executed in Naples, since the drawing appears to be from the same sketchbook as many of the sketches for works in Naples.

NAPLES, Cathedral, Cappella di S. Gennaro
THE HEAVENLY HOST

Fresco in the dome, painted in the first half of the 1640's. Reproduced Voss, p. 231.

188. STUDY FOR A PUTTO   (5717)

171 × 244 mm. Black and white chalk on grey-green paper.

The drawing corresponds closely with one of the figures round the lower edge of the dome.

NAPLES, SS. Apostoli

Fresco decoration of choir, crossing and nave. Painted between 1638 and 1644 (cf. Passeri, ed. Hess, p. 156 note 3).

The 600 drawings attributed to Lanfranco in the Museo di Capodimonte, Naples, include a number of studies connected with these frescoes and others are in the Louvre and at Besançon (cf. catalogue of the exhibition *Dessins romains du XVIIe siècle* at the Louvre, 1959, No.15).

THE FOUR EVANGELISTS

Frescoes in the pendentives of the crossing. Two of the frescoes (*St. Mark* and *St. Luke*) are engraved by Saint-Non in *Voyage Pittoresque ou Description des Royaumes de Naples et de Sicile*, Paris, 1781–85, i, Pl. opp. p. 113.

189. STUDY FOR AN EVANGELIST   (5675)

Circular, 159 mm. in diameter. Pen and brown ink.

In style close to the drawing for the *Martyrdom of St. Matthew* (No.194) and probably a first idea for the St. Matthew in one of the crossing pendentives. Two other drawings in the British Museum (1895-9-15-727, 728) seem also to be for these pendentives.

190. STUDY FOR ST. MARK   (5697)

367 × 251 mm. Black chalk, with touches of white, on buff paper.

STUDIES FOR ST. LUKE

191. 375 × 219 mm. Black chalk, heightened with white, on light-grey paper.   (2102)

From the Carracci volumes.

192. 333×251 mm. Black and white chalk on blue-grey paper. Squared in red chalk.   (5683)

Verso: Studies of a left arm and shoulder and a seated Monk.

These three drawings differ considerably from the executed paintings, but the fact that St. Luke holds a tablet in both Nos.191 and 192, and the similarity of the pose of the head in No.192, seem to connect the drawings with the frescoes. In No.190 the pose is close to that of St. Mark, particularly if one assumes that the axis of the drawing has been changed.

193. STUDY FOR THE LOWER HALF OF A FIGURE SUP-PORTED BY A PUTTO ON CLOUDS   (5687)

319×221 mm. Black and white chalk on grey paper. Squared.

Verso: Studies for a foot and drapery.

The figure cannot be identified, but it is probably the lower half of an Evangelist for a pendentive, and since its style, paper and technique show that it belongs to the Naples period, it may well be connected with one of the figures at the crossing of the SS. Apostoli.

THE MARTYRDOM OF ST. MATTHEW

Fresco in the right half of the lunette on the wall over the west door. Engraved by P. Petrini.

194. STUDY FOR THE WHOLE COMPOSITION (*Fig. 35*)   (5674)

354×233 mm. Pen and brown ink with grey wash, over black chalk. Squared.

In the fresco itself this scene, originally designed for the left half of the lunette, was transferred to the right. A pentiment shows how Lanfranco planned this alteration.

195. STUDY FOR THE HEAD AND SHOULDERS OF A SOLDIER   (5680)

251×184 mm. Black chalk, heightened with white, on grey paper.

Verso: A head.

The head on the *verso* is very close to one on the extreme left of the *Pentecost* at Fermo (cf. No.186), but it cannot be widely separated in time from the *recto*, and so the likeness is probably due to Lanfranco's regular habit of repeating models or poses at long intervals.

THE MARTYRDOM OF ST. SIMON

Fresco in the left half of the lunette on the wall over the west door.

196. STUDIES FOR THE PRINCIPAL GROUP   (5670)

181×172 mm. Pen and brown ink with grey wash. Inscribed at the top left: *lanfranco.*

Three studies for the group, with the Saint dragged to martyrdom.

APOSTLES AND PROPHETS

The upper parts of the nave wall over the arcade are decorated with a series of standing and seated figures of

Fig. 35   Cat. No. 194

Apostles and Prophets. These are impossible to identify, owing to the vagueness of their attributes and, in some cases, the bad condition of the frescoes.

197. STUDY FOR A PROPHET (*Plate 7*)   (5686)

375×252 mm. Black and white chalk on grey-green paper.

Verso: Study for a seated half-draped male figure.

Study for a figure in one of the lunettes on the right-hand side of the nave. Two drawings by Maratta (Nos.297 and 298) are almost identical in pose with this and suggest that he must have known either the fresco or this drawing. Since the Albani collection, from which the Lanfranco's almost certainly came, included Maratta's own collection, he may actually have owned this and other drawings by Lanfranco.

198. STUDY FOR ONE OF THE APOSTLES   (5688)

407×269 mm. Black and white chalk on grey-green paper. Squared.

199. STUDY FOR ST. THOMAS (*Plate 6*)   (5693)

412×223 mm. Black chalk, touches of white, on dark grey-green paper. Squared.

The drawing corresponds exactly with an engraving by F.

de Louvemont from a drawing by H. Trudus after Lanfranco, which is part of a series of the twelve Apostles published by Jacobus Raillardus in Naples in 1690 (the date on the *St. Peter*). The engravings seem to be based on Lanfranco's frescoes in the SS. Apostoli and in S. Martino (see below), and the present figure is like but not identical with one in the former church.

NAPLES, Certosa di S. Martino, Church
Frescoes on walls of nave. Executed 1637–39 (cf. Passeri, ed. Hess, p. 156).

STUDIES FOR STANDING FIGURES
200. 393 × 213 mm. Black and white chalk on dark grey paper.   (5694)

201. 361 × 240 mm. Black and white chalk on grey-green paper. Squared.   (5702)
Verso: Two studies of hands.

202. 393 × 213 mm. Black and white chalk on grey paper.
Verso: Study of a seated figure.   (5684)

These three drawings correspond fairly closely with three of the standing figures on the walls of the nave, the identity of which is not easy to establish, owing to their lack of attributes.

PARMA, Galleria Nazionale
ST. PETER HEALING ST. AGATHA
Painted about 1614–15 (cf. *Maestri della Pittura del Seicento Emiliano*, Bologna, 1959, p. 225, No.115, and Pl. 115).

203. STUDY FOR THE HEAD OF ST. PETER   (5681)
239 × 209 mm. Black and white chalk, on grey-green paper.
Verso: Studies of a horse and a hand.
The head on the *recto* and the hand on the *verso* correspond closely to the painting. The drawing of the horse does not seem to be connected.

CHRIST IN GLORY WITH SAINTS
Probably painted c.1610 (cf. Passeri, ed. Hess, p. 153 note 3). Reproduced in *Aurea Parma*, 1931, p.218.

204. STUDY FOR THE FIGURE OF A SAINT   (2103)
379 × 213 mm. Black and white chalk on grey-green paper. From the Carracci volumes.

ROME, St. Peter's, Cappella della Pietà
SCENES FROM THE PASSION
Executed between 1629 and 1632 (cf. Waterhouse, p. 77).

THE ADORATION OF THE CROSS
Fresco in centre of ceiling.
205. STUDIES FOR AN ANGEL   (5711)
396 × 217 mm. Black and white chalk on grey-brown paper.
Verso: Study for the same figure.
A drawing of the same head is in the Scholz collection, New York.

206. STUDY FOR AN ANGEL   (5706)
350 × 221 mm. Black and white chalk on grey-brown paper. Squared in red chalk.
Verso: Studies of heads and an arm.
Exh.: Burlington Fine Arts Club, 1925, No.16; *17th Century Art*, Royal Academy, London, 1938, No.415.
The same figure occurs, in reverse, in the *Transfiguration* in the Certosa di S. Martino, Naples. The figure studies on the *verso* are for the same fresco as those on the *recto*.

CHRIST CROWNED WITH THORNS
Fresco on the end wall of the right wing of the chapel.

207. STUDY FOR A KNEELING FIGURE   (5698)
383 × 262 mm. Black and white chalk on dark grey-brown paper.

CHRIST SHOWN TO THE PEOPLE
Fresco ceiling of right wing.

208. STUDY FOR AN ATTENDANT   (5716)
297 × 197 mm. Black and white chalk on green-grey paper.
Verso: Study of a female head.
The *verso* study is for the *Adoration of the Cross* in the main dome of the chapel.

CHRIST BEFORE PILATE
Ceiling of right wing.

209. STUDY FOR A DRAPED MALE FIGURE   (5696)
335 × 232 mm. Black and white chalk on grey-green paper.

CHRIST MOCKED
Ceiling of left wing.

210. STUDY FOR THE FIGURE OF CHRIST   (5718)
189 × 260 mm. Black and white chalk on grey-brown paper.
A similar figure occurs on the vaulting of the Sacchetti Chapel in S. Giovanni dei Fiorentini (engraved by D. Cunego).

211. STUDY OF A WOMAN STANDING WITH ONE ARM
OUTSTRETCHED (*Plate 5*)   (5701)
390 × 230 mm. Black and white chalk, detail in red, on grey-brown paper. Squared.
Verso: Drapery study.

212. STUDIES OF A MAN LEANING FORWARD AND A
HAND   (5692)
355 × 229 mm. Black and white chalk on grey-brown paper.
Verso: Studies of legs and a female head.

213. STUDY OF A HAND   (5721)
158 × 247 mm. Black and white chalk on grey-brown paper.

214. STUDY OF THE HEAD OF AN OLD MAN   (5679)
376 × 238 mm. Black and white chalk on light brown paper.

Verso: Drapery studies.

These four drawings are so exactly similar in style, paper and technique to the series for St. Peter's that they are likely to have been made in preparation for the same chapel. The frescoes are now so much damaged that it is often hard to distinguish the figures and a final identification is therefore impossible.

ROME, Convent of the Barefooted Carmelites

THE MADONNA GIVING THE HABIT OF THE CARMELITE ORDER TO ST. THERESA

The painting was executed about 1612–13 for the church of S. Giuseppe (cf. *Burl. Mag.*, xciv, 1952, pp. 195, and 193, Fig. 8).

215. STUDY FOR LOWER HALF OF A DRAPED FIGURE, SEATED AND SUPPORTED BY A PUTTO   (5703)

238 × 328 mm. Black and white chalk on blue paper.

Probably a study for the figure of the Madonna.

ROME, Quirinal, Sala dei Corazzieri

Lanfranco's share in the fresco decorations of this room was executed c.1611–12 (cf. Waterhouse, p. 77).

216. STUDY FOR AN *IGNUDO* (*Plate 4*)   (5700)

385 × 224 mm. Black and white chalk on green-grey paper.

Verso: Study of a male figure with hands raised.

217. STUDY OF A STANDING PUTTO   (5719)

276 × 181 mm. Black and white chalk on grey paper.

Verso: Studies of hands, one holding the hilt of a sword.

These two drawings are studies for the decorative elements in the Sala dei Corazzieri. In style and draughtsmanship they show strong traces of Lanfranco's training under the Carracci.

2. Drawings connected with engraved works

218. THE TRANSFIGURATION (*Fig. 36*)   (5667)

377 × 258 mm. Pen and brown wash, heightened with body-colour, on brown paper. Inscribed: *Lanfranco.*

The top three figures agree closely, in reverse, with the engraving by Claudio Dagli (or d'Aglio) after Lanfranco, dated 1641, for the title-page to an edition of St. Thomas Aquinas' *Evangeliorum Quadragesimalium Decas Prima*, published in Rome. The lower part of the composition is replaced by figures of St. Thomas, two Dominican monks, and the symbols of the Evangelists.

The drawing is entirely unlike Lanfranco's work about 1641, when he was in Naples, and one may wonder whether the Roman publisher did not use some much earlier drawing which happened to come into his possession. This would account for the strong elements of Mannerism, particularly in the drawing of hands and eyes.

219. STUDY FOR ST. HUBERT   (5705)

342 × 273 mm. Black and white chalk on grey-brown paper.

The pose is similar to that of the Saint in an anonymous

Fig. 36   Cat. No. 218

engraving after Lanfranco (*Joan. Lanfrancus invent.*), published by Le Blond, where, however, he is old and bearded. The drawing may, therefore, be from a *garzone* in preparation for the engraved composition.

3. Drawings not connected with known works.

220. THE VIRGIN AND CHILD ACCOMPANIED BY A SAINT APPEARING TO A MONK   (5668)

237 × 126 mm. Pen and brown wash. Squared. On two pieces of paper.

Similar in style to the study for the *Martyrdom of St. Matthew* (No.194), and probably dating from the Neapolitan period.

221. STUDY OF A MONK   (5685)

366 × 252 mm. Black and white chalk on grey paper.

Verso: Studies of draperies.

222. STUDY OF A KNEELING MONK   (5710)

396 × 254 mm. Black and white chalk on grey paper.

Verso: Study for standing male figure.

223. STUDY OF A STANDING MAN   (5707)

384 × 262 mm. Black and white chalk on grey-green paper.

Verso: Study of a reclining man.

Fig. 37   Cat. No. 230

**224. STUDY FOR A STANDING MALE FIGURE WITH
ARMS RAISED** (5695)
373 × 260 mm. Black and white chalk on grey paper.
Verso: Studies of hands.

225. STUDY OF AN APOSTLE (5690)
364 × 246 mm. Black and white chalk on grey paper.
Verso: Study for the same figure.

226. STUDY OF DRAPERY (5708)
366 × 268 mm. Black and white chalk on brown paper.
Verso: Study of part of a male head.

227. STUDY FOR A SEATED MALE FIGURE (5689)
360 × 254 mm. Black and white chalk on grey paper.
Verso: Study for a standing male figure. Squared.

These seven drawings are similar in style, technique, format
and paper to those made for SS. Apostoli and S. Martino,
and therefore probably belong to the Neapolitan period.

228. STUDY OF THE HEAD OF AN OLD MAN (5678)
190 × 179 mm. Black and white chalk on grey-green paper.
Perhaps connected with the frescoes in S. Agostino, Rome
(cf. Bollettino d'Arte, XLIV, 1959, pp. 337 ff.; Figs. 1 and 2).

229. STUDY OF A HEAD (5682)
238 × 181 mm. Black and white chalk on brown paper.

230. STUDY OF THE HEAD OF AN OLD MAN (*Fig. 37*) (5347)
357 × 253 mm. Black and white chalk on grey-brown paper.

231. A SAINT AND OTHER FIGURES (5676)
Circular, 165 mm. in diameter. Pen and brown ink.

232. A FEMALE SAINT SUPPORTED BY PUTTI ON CLOUDS
(5669)
301 × 227 mm. Red chalk. The paper is made up of three
pieces joined together.
Verso: Three studies of Angels and clouds. Red chalk.

Perhaps a preliminary sketch for the *Assumption* in S. Agostino,
Rome (cf. Bollettino d'Arte, XLIV, 1959, p. 337, Fig. 1); but
a very similar sketch is in the British Museum (1895–9–15–
927 *verso*) on the back of a drawing which is apparently
connected with the pendentives of the SS. Apostoli.

GIOVANNI LANFRANCO
(attributed to)

233. STUDY FOR AN APOSTLE (?ST. PAUL) (2068)
396 × 219 mm. Black chalk, with touches of white, on blue
paper.
From the Carracci volumes.
Close in style to Lanfranco's early drawings.

234. STUDY OF A SLEEPING SOLDIER (5691)
356 × 251 mm. Black and white chalk on grey-brown paper.
Presumably a study for a *Resurrection.*

235. STUDY OF A FLYING ANGEL (2050)
228 × 333 mm. Black and white chalk on grey-green paper.
From the Carracci volumes.
Close in style to Lanfranco's early drawings.

236. FIGURE STUDIES (1940)
241 × 200 mm. Black and white chalk on grey paper.
Inscribed: *L. Caracci.*
From the Carracci volumes.
Possibly by Lanfranco in his early period.

237. A SEATED FIGURE HOLDING A PILGRIM'S STAFF
433 × 358 mm. Red chalk on brown paper. (6115)

238. STUDY OF A SEATED BOY, WEARING A CLOAK
(3462)
350 × 305 mm. Black chalk, heightened with white, on
greenish paper.
Inv. A, p. 80: 'Guido &c.'.

239. STUDY OF A NUDE MODEL (5713)
400 × 269 mm. Black and white chalk on grey-brown paper.

Fig. 38   Cat. No. 245

Exh.: Royal Academy, London, 1950–51, No.429.
Probably made as a study for a dead Christ. Not entirely consistent with Lanfranco's certain drawings.

240. STUDY OF A MAN ON A LADDER   (2045)
332 × 219 mm. Black chalk on grey paper.
From the Carracci volumes.
Probably a study for a *Descent from the Cross.*

241. STUDY OF A KNEELING FIGURE   (5666)
205 × 145 mm. Black chalk, touches of white, on grey paper.
Inscribed at foot: *Lanfranco.*

GIOVANNI LANFRANCO
(follower of)

242. THREE SLEEPING APOSTLES   (3580)
210 × 254 mm. Black and white chalk on blue-grey paper.
Study for an *Agony in the Garden.*

FILIPPO LAURI
(1623–94)

GIDEON AND THE FLEECE

243. 335 × 239 mm. Oval. Pen and brown ink, with brown and grey wash, on white paper, much discoloured. Damaged and mended.   (4538)

244. 337 × 236 mm. The composition in a drawn oval. Pen and brown ink, with brown and grey wash. *(Fig. 39)* (4537)

Inv. A, p. 111: '. . . Gideon with the Fleece. Two drawings suppos'd by Filippo Laura . . .'

Studies for the painting in the Sala Augusta in the Quirinal, traditionally attributed to Salvator Rosa on the authority of Pascoli and Titi, but, as was pointed out verbally by N. Wibiral, actually by Filippo Lauri, to whom the two drawings are ascribed in Inventory A. The ascription of the painting to Lauri is confirmed by Baldinucci in a manuscript *Life,* recently published by B. Riccio (*Commentari,* x, 1959,

p. 9. The painting is reproduced on Pl. i, Fig. 1). A payment of 1657 to Lauri for work in the Quirinal gives a precise date for the painting.
In No.243 the figure of Gideon corresponds more closely to the painting than in No.244, but in both drawings the group of sleeping figures differs considerably from the painting.

245. DESIGN FOR A CEILING (*Fig. 38*)   (6833)
255 × 735 mm. Pen and brown wash, with water-colour added in the roundels.

Fig. 39   Cat. No. 244

Fig. 40   Cat. No. 250

Study for a ceiling of a room in the Palazzo Borghese, painted by Lauri in 1671 according to Baldinucci (cf. Riccio, *op. cit.*, p. 11; details of the ceiling are reproduced on Pls. iii and iv, Figs. 4–8). The drawing shows a section of the cove, with a rectangular panel which is blank, and two circular ones, which show the stories of Mercury and Argus in one and Alpheus and Arethusa in the other. In the fresco itself the rectangular panel was left out and the poses of the *ignudi* flanking the circular ones were changed.

FILIPPO LAURI
(attributed to)

246. ST. LAWRENCE DISTRIBUTING ALMS   (4544)
207 × 231 mm. Black chalk.

247. ST. LAWRENCE LED AWAY TO MARTYRDOM (4545)
212 × 261 mm. Black chalk.

248. THE FLAGELLATION OF ST. LAWRENCE   (4546)
212 × 269 mm. Black chalk.

249. THE MARTYRDOM OF ST. LAWRENCE   (4547)
212 × 254 mm. Black chalk.

These four drawings, almost identical in format and technique and forming a series, have all the same mannerisms as one of the *Martyrdom of St. Stephen* at Chatsworth, with an old and convincing attribution to Filippo Lauri.

GIOVANNI BATTISTA LENARDI
(1656–1704)

250. FIGURES RECORDING THE MONUMENTS OF ANTI-QUITY (*Fig. 40*)   (6814)
312 × 229 mm. Pen and brown ink, black wash over red chalk. Inscribed: *Di Gio. Batista Lenardi.*

Exact study for the title-page to Giovanni Ciampini's *Vetera Monumenta*, Rome, 1690.

Two girls draw the monuments of Antiquity, attacked by Time, while another writes a description of them in a book, and a fourth selects the type with which to print what the third is writing. The engraving is reversed, and in it the standing figure on the right in the drawing is moved to a more central position over the seated girl drawing an arch.

251. THE PRESENTATION IN THE TEMPLE   (6810)
362 × 255 mm. Black and white chalk on grey-brown paper. Inscribed: *Gio : Batt.ª Lennardi.*

The drawing is consistent with the style of Lenardi as shown, for instance, in Caylus' engraving after a drawing of the *Pentecost* in the Crozat collection.

OTTAVIO LEONI
(c.1578–1630)

252. PORTRAIT OF A WOMAN   (5184)
210 × 143 mm. Black, red and white chalk on grey-green paper.

253. PORTRAIT OF A WOMAN IN A WIDOW'S CAP (5185)
219 × 147 mm. Black and red chalk on grey-green paper. Inscribed on the mount: *Lioni* in an early nineteenth-century hand.

The drawings are laid down, so that it is impossible to read the inscriptions which partly show through from the *verso*. Both are consistent with Leoni's usual style.

ANDREA LOCATELLI
(1695–1741)

254. LANDSCAPE WITH MEN FISHING IN A RIVER (6154)
299 × 524 mm. Pen and brown ink.

The name of Locatelli was apparently written on the old mount, and the drawing is like many of Locatelli's paintings in general composition and in the placing of the figures fishing.

CARLO MARATTA
(1625–1713)

Almost all the drawings here catalogued come from six volumes recorded in Inventory A as containing drawings by Maratta, which can be identified as Nos.4091–4333 and 4345–4395, though a few have been added from other volumes devoted to the artist's pupils, and some from miscellaneous volumes. Nos.4090 and 4334–4344 were inserted loose in these volumes.

Apart from the series in the Louvre the Maratta drawings in the Royal Collection form the most important group known. Their history is not clear, though it can be assumed that they come from the Albani collection. It is possible that some of them formed part of the drawings sold by Maratta to Clement XI in 1703 (cf. J. Pope-Hennessy, *The Drawings of Domenichino at Windsor Castle*, 1948, p. 10), but on the whole this is not likely. As far as we can judge, the transaction mainly concerned drawings by earlier masters which Maratta had collected, and it is not likely that he would have parted with his own drawings while he was still working actively. On the whole it is more probable that the series was bought by the Pope during the eight years which separated his own death in 1721 from that of the artist.

The series is of great importance both for its quality and for the light which it throws on Maratta's methods. More than 60 drawings—mostly originals—can be related to known works, and a high percentage of the remainder can be attributed to Maratta himself with reasonable certainty. They cover the whole range of his work, from the early drawings in the manner of his master Sacchi to the freest and boldest sketches of the late period.

They also include a large number of drawings after the Antique and after the artists of the sixteenth and early seventeenth centuries. Most of these were made by Maratta or his pupils as a part of their training, and it is interesting to notice which masters are chosen as models: first and foremost Raphael, but also Michelangelo and Correggio in the sixteenth century, and the Carracci, Domenichino and Guido Reni from the early seventeenth. Some of the drawings after Raphael's frescoes in the Vatican were undertaken in connection with the restoration commissioned from the artist by Clement XI. In certain cases these record the frescoes before the restoration, and they may therefore provide evidence of interest for students of Raphael. Maratta's admiration for Raphael is well known, and it is not without significance that a drawing by him was found in the volumes which contained Maratta's own works (cf. Popham and Wilde, p. 309, No. 788).

The Windsor Marattas should provide a basis for the study of his style as a draughtsman and for distinguishing his drawings from those of his pupils, but it must be emphasised that at present this distinction is still hard to make, and there may well be occasion to re-distribute many of the borderline cases as knowledge of the subject increases.

1. Drawings connected with known works

ANCONA, Pinacoteca
THE MADONNA WITH ST. AMBROSE AND TWO OTHER SAINTS

Painted about 1672 (cf. F. H. Dowley, *Burl. Mag.*, ci, 1959, p. 66, and Pl. 64).

255. STUDY FOR ST. AMBROSE   (4137)

310 × 208 mm. Red chalk, with touches of white, on blue-grey paper.

Another drawing for the Saint is in the Uffizi (cf. Dowley, *op. cit.*, p. 70).

BÜCKEBURG, Schloss
THE BIRTH OF THE VIRGIN

Painted c.1685 for S. Maria dell' Anima, Rome (cf. Voss, p. 596, and repr. p. 340).

256. STUDY FOR ST. ANNE   (4135)

260 × 410 mm. Red chalk on blue-grey paper.

COPENHAGEN, Museum
LA TINTURA DELLA ROSA

The painting is reproduced in the catalogue of the exhibition of *Italienische Malerei des 17. und 18. Jahrhunderts*, Wiesbaden, 1935, No.131, and shows Venus turning round in alarm at finding that she has pricked her foot on a thorn.

257. STUDY FOR THE HEAD AND THE UPPER HALF OF THE FIGURE OF VENUS   (4227)

237 × 201 mm. Red chalk.

THE WHOLE COMPOSITION

258. 158 × 178 mm. Red chalk.   (4173)

259. 162 × 219 mm. Red chalk.   (4100)

Engraved by Ryland in 1763 for Rogers, *A collection of prints in imitation of drawings*, 1778, i, p. 165.

The two last drawings show different versions of the story. In No.258 Venus is pulling the thorn from her foot, and in No.259 it is being pulled out by a putto, but in view of the similarity in types and poses both drawings probably represent ideas produced in connection with the painting and rejected by the artist.

A drawing showing a different version of the last theme is in the Witt Collection, Courtauld Institute of Art (No.208), engraved by Ryland in 1763.

DRESDEN, Gallery
MADONNA WITH THE CHRIST CHILD ASLEEP

Engraved by Daullé and acquired in 1743 from Algarotti. Voss (p. 600) maintains that it is a late work.

260. STUDY FOR THE WHOLE COMPOSITION *(Fig. 41)*   (6096)

312 × 252 mm. Black and white chalk on grey-green paper. Squared.

The drawing is traditionally ascribed to Sassoferrato, but the connection with the painting, which is certainly by Maratta, is indubitable, and in fact, although technically the drawing is a skilful pastiche of Sassoferrato, the sentiment is different from his and suggests a later generation.

Fig. 41   Cat. No. 260

There is no external evidence that Maratta imitated Sasso-ferrato, but given the fact that he was trained in the studio of Sacchi, the least Baroque painter of his generation in Rome, there is nothing improbable in his having admired Sassoferrato. It is, on the other hand, likely that he did so in his youth rather than in his later years, and both painting and drawing should, in spite of Voss' opinion, be dated early. The style of the painting supports this hypothesis. For another drawing in exactly the same manner, cf. No. 328

FLORENCE, Corsini Collection
ST. JAMES

One of a set representing the Apostles painted for Cardinal Antonio Barberini about 1661 (cf. A. Mezzetti, 'Contributi a Carlo Maratti', *Rivista dell' Istituto Nazionale d'Archeologia e Storia dell' Arte*, N.S., iv, 1955, p. 323).

261. STUDY FOR THE WHOLE PAINTING   (4169)

353 × 237 mm. Black chalk.

The figure agrees with the painting, except for a slight dif-ference in the pose of the pointing arm, but it is in reverse. Perhaps an offset.

FLORENCE, Pitti
THE VIRGIN AND CHILD
APPEARING TO ST. PHILIP NERI

Painted for S. Giovanni dei Fiorentini shortly before 1675, when it is mentioned by Titi (reproduced in Voss, p. 338).

262. STUDY FOR THE WHOLE COMPOSITION   (5553)

254 × 164 mm. Red chalk.

From the Bernini volumes.

The drawing does not show the figures of St. Peter, St. Paul and the Magdalene, which appear in the painting, but it is probably a first idea for the composition.

FORLI, Gallery
THE MADONNA AND CHILD
APPEARING TO ST. FRANCIS OF SALES

263. STUDY FOR ST. FRANCIS   (4128)

419 × 279 mm. Red chalk, with touches of white, on blue paper.

Exact study for the painting, except that the figure is not bearded.

GENOA, S. Maria di Carignano
THE MARTYRDOM OF ST. BLAISE
AND ST. SEBASTIAN

Painted shortly after 1680 for S. Carlo ai Catinari, Rome (cf. Voss, p. 596; reproduced p. 339).

264. STUDY FOR ST. SEBASTIAN   (4126)

396 × 288 mm. Black chalk, with touches of white, on paper partly prepared with a tempera wash.

265. STUDY FOR THE MAN PULLING ON A ROPE (*Plate 59*)
                                            (4170)

391 × 235 mm. Red chalk, with touches of white, on yellowish-grey paper.

GERMANY, Private Collection
ST. LUKE PAINTING THE VIRGIN

A painting recorded as passing through various German sales (Wenstenberg sale, Berlin, 1908, lot 66; Ober-Morlen sale, Frankfort, 7.x.1920, lot 441; Hahn sale, 17.iii.1936, lot 109), showing St. Anthony of Padua contemplating St. Luke painting the Virgin.

266. STUDY FOR THE VIRGIN AND ST. LUKE   (4151)

241 × 185 mm. Red chalk on buff paper.

The drawing shows St. Luke in almost exactly the same pose, but does not include St. Anthony. A highly finished drawing in the Bloxham Collection, Rugby School, is a variant of No. 266.

KNOWSLEY, Earl of Derby Collection
ST. ANTHONY OF PADUA
ADORING THE VIRGIN AND CHILD

Engraved by H. Winstanley in 1729.

267. STUDY FOR THE WHOLE COMPOSITION   (4144)

366 × 245 mm. Red chalk.

In the painting the Child sits on the Virgin's lap and hands the lily to St. Anthony.

Fig. 42   Cat. No. 272 *recto*

Fig. 43   Cat. No. 272 *verso*

LENINGRAD, Hermitage
HOLY FAMILY (305)

268. STUDY FOR THE HEAD OF THE VIRGIN   (4159)

357 × 248 mm. Black chalk.

Highly finished study. In the painting the Virgin does not look down so much, and the drawing may have been cut crooked.

Formerly LONDON, Duke of Westminster Collection
HAGAR AND ISHMAEL

The painting, upright in format, was sold at Christie's (4.vii.1924, lot 16) and was later with Brunner, Paris. A slightly different version was engraved by Audenaerd.

STUDIES FOR THE WHOLE COMPOSITION

269. 384 × 478 mm. Red chalk.   (4093)

270. 499 × 335 mm. Red chalk.   (4353)

Both drawings differ substantially from the composition mentioned above and must be either preliminary versions, or later variants. In No.269 Hagar faces left, whereas in No.270 she faces right in a strictly profile view, and the poses of both Ishmael and the angel are also different.
Other drawings of the same subject are at Chatsworth and at Düsseldorf (1536).
The figures in No.269 are related to Francesco Cozzas' versions of the same subject (cf. *Paragone*, vii, 1956, No.83, Figs. 35, 36).

NEW HAVEN, Conn., Yale University Gallery
THE FLIGHT INTO EGYPT

271. THE WHOLE COMPOSITION   (4360)

387 × 268 mm. Red chalk. Inscribed: *Carlo Marati* in the 'deceptive hand'.

A copy after the painting, which is attributed, without obvious reason, to Trevisani.

ROME, S. Andrea al Quirinale
THE VISION OF ST. STANISLAS KOTSKA

Waterhouse (p. 79) states that the painting was executed shortly before 1697, when it first appears in the Guides. It must, however, have been painted earlier, since the engraving after it by Dorigny is dated 1689. A variant is at Hampton Court.

272. DRAWING OF THE WHOLE COMPOSITION (*Fig. 42*)
                                              (4154)

497 × 375 mm. Red chalk.

Verso: A design for a tomb. Pen and brown ink. (*Fig. 43*)

The drawing differs considerably from the painting, but contains the essential features of it: the Saint who holds the Christ Child which he has received from the Virgin, the lily in the foreground, the putti and the flying angels.
The *verso* drawing is of importance as being one of Maratta's rare designs for sculpture in an architechtural setting.

ROME, S. Carlo al Corso
ST. CHARLES BORROMEO RECEIVED
INTO GLORY
Painted c.1685–90 (cf. Waterhouse, p. 79).

273. STUDY FOR THE FIGURE OF CHRIST   (4123)

270×393 mm. Red chalk, with touches of white, on blue-grey paper.

274. STUDY FOR THE ANGEL HOLDING THE CROZIER
                                              (4122)
259×194 mm. Red chalk, with touches of white, on greenish-grey paper.

275. STUDY FOR ST. AMBROSE   (4136)

411×269 mm. Red chalk, with touches of white.

A nude study from a youthful model for the pose of the Saint. A study for the head of St. Charles is in the Barber Institute, Birmingham.

ROME, Gesù
THE AGONY OF ST. FRANCIS XAVIER
Commissioned 1674 (cf. Waterhouse, p. 79).

276. STUDIES OF TWO BOYS   (4130)

375×258 mm. Red chalk, with touches of white, on grey-green paper.

One study is for the kneeling boy in the foreground. The other figure does not occur in the painting.

ROME, S. Isidoro, Cappella Alaleona
ST. JOSEPH IN GLORY
Fresco in the dome, finished 1652 (cf. Waterhouse, p. 79).

277. HEAD OF KING DAVID   (4164)

444×367 mm. Black chalk, with touches of white, on blue paper.

278. HEAD OF ST. JOSEPH (*Plate 56*)   (4165)

302×298 mm. Black and white chalk on blue paper.

279. HEAD OF A WOMAN   (4163)

304×262 mm. Black chalk on blue paper, with touches of red and white chalk.

Study for the woman next to King David.

ROME, S. Isidoro, Cappella Ludovisi
THE AGONY IN THE GARDEN
Begun after 1652 and finished before 1657 (cf. Waterhouse, p. 79).

280. DRAWING OF THE HEAD OF THE ANGEL   (4217)

243×182 mm. Red chalk.

Probably a school drawing after the painting.

ROME, S. Isidoro, Chapel to the right of the High Altar
MADONNA
Painted c.1663 (cf. Waterhouse, p. 79).

281. HEAD OF THE MADONNA   (4211)

259×184 mm. Red chalk.

Copy in reverse. Studio drawing.

282. HEADS OF THE MADONNA AND OF A YOUTH (4223)

255×147 mm. Red chalk.

The head of the Madonna is almost identical with the painting. The head of the youth is not connected. Studio drawing.

ROME, S. Maria di Montesanto
MADONNA WITH ST. FRANCIS
AND ST. JAMES
The painting was executed c.1686 (cf. Waterhouse, p. 80).

STUDIES FOR THE WHOLE COMPOSITION

283. 261×187 mm. Pen and bistre-wash over red chalk. (*Plate 54*)   (4150)

284. 315×201 mm. Red chalk. (*Plate 55*)   (4101)

Lit.: F. H. Dowley, *Art Quarterly*, xx, 1957, pp. 174 ff.

Another study for the whole composition is in Düsseldorf (cf. Dowley, *loc. cit.*), and a third was in the Leverton-Harris sale (Sotheby, 22.v.1928, lot 71).

285. STUDY FOR ST. JAMES   (4195)

255×176 mm. Red chalk.

Lit.: F. H. Dowley, *Art Quarterly*, xx, 1957, p. 179, note 38.

ROME, S. Maria del Popolo, Cappella Cibò
THE IMMACULATA WITH ST. GREGORY,
ST. CHRYSOSTOM, ST. JOHN
AND ST. AUGUSTINE
Painted c.1685–86 (cf. Waterhouse, p. 80).

286. STUDY FOR THE WHOLE COMPOSITION (*Plate 53*)
                                              (4096)
503×291 mm. Pen and brown ink over red chalk.

Lit.: F. H. Dowley, *Art Quarterly*, xx, 1957, pp. 171 ff.

The figures are more freely disposed than in the painting, with St. John on the right, St. Gregory in the middle, and the other two Fathers on the left.

Other drawings for the composition are in the Rudolf collection (cf. *Old Master Drawings*, x, 1935–6, Pl. 45); in the H. L. Cooke collection, Washington; at Düsseldorf; in the Pierpont Morgan Library; and in the Uffizi (cf. Dowley, *loc. cit.*). In addition, there is in the Uffizi a finished drawing, perhaps after the painting (No.8175, as Vouet). A study for the St. John is in Berlin (*Jahrbuch der preussischen Kunstsammlungen*, xxxv, 1914, p. 29, and Fig. 5), and another is in the British Museum; one for St. Gregory was formerly with F. A. Drey, London, and one for the St. Ambrose is in the Uffizi (*Burlington Magazine*, ci, 1959, p. 70, and Fig. 33); one for the head of St. Gregory is in the British Museum.

ROME, S. Maria in Vallicella
MADONNA WITH ST. IGNATIUS AND
ST. CHARLES BORROMEO
Painted c.1685 (cf. Waterhouse, p. 80).

287. STUDY FOR ST. CHARLES (*Plate 58*)   (4132)

389 × 249 mm. Red chalk, with touches of white, on blue-grey paper.

Drawings for the whole composition are in the Albertina and at Copenhagen.

ROME, St. Peter's
JUDITH AND HOLOFERNES

Mosaic in the second bay of the left aisle; executed c.1686. Engraved by Ferroni in 1705. A variant in oils is at Bückeburg (cf. Voss, p. 597).

288. STUDY FOR THE HEAD OF HOLOFERNES (*Plate 57*)
(4166)

330 × 256 mm. Red chalk, with touches of white, on blue-grey paper.

Other drawings are at Düsseldorf (Nos.174, 181).

FOUR PROPHETS AND KINGS

Mosaics in the pendentives of the third bay of the left aisle; executed after 1689 (cf. Waterhouse, p. 81).

289. KING DAVID   (4183)
241 × 170 mm. Red chalk.

290. ANOTHER KING   (4185)
241 × 172 mm. Red chalk.

291. A PROPHET   (4182)
244 × 173 mm. Red chalk.

292. A PROPHET   (4184)
245 × 172 mm. Red chalk.

Four feeble studio drawings (possibly offsets) connected with the pendentive mosaics. Only the *King David* corresponds reasonably closely. All are probably copies after early designs for the series.

ROME, St. Peter's, Aula della Benedizione
JAEL AND SISERA

Cartoon for the mosaic in the second bay of the left aisle; executed c.1686 (cf. Voss, p. 597).

THE WHOLE COMPOSITION

293. 260 × 197 mm. Black chalk on buff paper. (*Fig. 44*)
(4103)
294. 244 × 163 mm. Black chalk, pen and bistre-wash.
(4435)
No.294 is from a volume of Pietro de Pietri and others.

295. STUDY FOR THE HEAD OF JAEL   (4161)
91 × 91 mm. Red chalk.

No.293 shows the composition almost in its final stage, and is very close to Düsseldorf No.175.
No.295 is a study for the head of Jael. Other such studies are in the Pierpont Morgan Library (formerly Oppenheimer collection), and in the collection of H. Spensley, Melbourne. A finished drawing is in the British Museum (Pp. 5–126).
No.294 shows the composition enlarged from a lunette to a rectangular composition and includes on the right a soldier

Fig. 44   Cat. No. 293

leaning on a spear. It is, therefore, probably a first preparation for the composition, engraved by Ferroni in 1705. Since, however, this drawing shows the line of the lunette drawn across it, the process may have been reversed, and Maratta may first have imagined the whole composition and later cut it down to the lunette form. This drawing is unusual in style for Maratta, but in view of its connection with the compositions mentioned and of its high quality, it must be from his hand.
Another drawing connected with the lunette composition is at Düsseldorf (No.176).

ELIJAH

Cartoon for the mosaic in the second bay of the left aisle (cf. Waterhouse, p. 81).

296. STUDY FOR THE HEAD   (4118)
229 × 269 mm. Black chalk.

A very similar head occurs in one of the kneeling kings in the *Adoration of the Magi* in S. Marco, Rome, engraved by Frey.

AN EVANGELIST

Cartoon for the mosaic in the second bay of the left aisle.

STUDIES FOR THE WHOLE FIGURE

297. 420 × 269 mm. Red chalk, heightened with white on blue paper. (*Fig. 45*)   (4124)
298. 419 × 267 mm. Red chalk, heightened with white, on blue paper.   (4125)

Fig. 45   Cat. No. 297

These two drawings, which are for a spandrel design, are strikingly similar to one by Lanfranco (No.197), which Maratta may have owned. A further drawing for the same figure, almost identical with No.298, was with Colnaghi in 1949 (exhibition, No.56). No.297 shows the figure in the nude; the other two are both clothed.

ROME, Capitoline Gallery
THE VIRGIN, CHRIST AND ST. JOSEPH

299. STUDY FOR THE FIGURES OF THE VIRGIN AND CHILD   (4105)

497×380 mm. Cut to an octagon. Black chalk on grey-brown paper.

St. John kisses the foot of Christ, who sits on the Virgin's lap. An almost identical but somewhat freer drawing was in the collection of the Rev. C. Goodenough as by Maratta, and was bequeathed by him to the British Museum, where it is ascribed to Niccolò Berettoni (1923–1–13–29). No.299 is probably a fair copy after it, and both drawings seem to be by Maratta. The pose and action of the Christ Child are identical with the painting, and the Madonna has many similarities, but the drawing shows the infant St. John kissing the foot of the Christ Child, a motive which does not appear

in the painting. On the other hand, the painting shows on the right St. Joseph, who does not appear in the drawing.

ROME, Galleria Nazionale
PORTRAIT OF CARDINAL ANTONIO BARBERINI

Probably painted in the early 1660's (cf. Waterhouse, p. 79).

300. STUDY OF THE HEAD (*Plate 60*)   (4162)

238×179 mm. Red chalk.

Lit.: A. Blunt, *Journal of the Warburg and Courtauld Institutes,* xxi, 1958, p. 287.

ROME, Quirinal
ADORATION OF THE SHEPHERDS

The original was painted in 1657 for the Gallery of the Quirinal Palace. It is now covered, but is known in two replicas in the Louvre and the Hermitage (cf. Voss, p. 595).

301. STUDIES OF CHERUBS' HEADS AND HANDS (4475)

190×299 mm. Black and red chalk, heightened with white, on grey-blue paper.

From the Cortona volumes.

Some of the heads correspond exactly to those in the painting, and one of the other sketches is a study for Joseph's right hand.

A drawing for the whole composition is in the Ashmolean Museum, Oxford (No.899).

Fig. 46   Cat. No. 302

ROME, Palazzo Rospigliosi
ST. PHILIP NERI ADORING A PAINTING OF THE VIRGIN SHOWN TO HIM BY AN ANGEL

The painting, in a room on the top floor of the palace, was engraved by Jacob Frey.

302. STUDY FOR THE WHOLE COMPOSITION (*Fig. 46*)
(4149)
206 × 156 mm. Oval. Pen and brown wash over red chalk.

303. HEAD OF A BABY   (4133 *verso*)
360 × 250 mm. Brown chalk, heightened with white, on grey paper.

Recto: Studies of hands.

Two studies of hands, which are very close in character to those of the Saint, but slightly different in pose. See also No. 331.

SIENA, Chigi Collection
THE FLIGHT INTO EGYPT

The painting in Siena Cathedral, executed in the late 1650's for Alexander VII, is now replaced by a mosaic; the original belongs to the Chigi family.

304. HEAD OF ST. JOSEPH AND OTHER STUDIES   (4194)
192 × 285 mm. Red chalk.

The head of the bearded man is almost identical with that of St. Joseph, though it is of a type which frequently occurs in Maratta's work (cf. for instance a *Holy Family*, dated 1676, in the collection of the Duke of Buccleuch at Boughton). Probably a studio drawing after the painting.

2. Drawings connected with engraved compositions

305. TOBIAS LEAVING HIS FAMILY   (4142)
248 × 383 mm. Black chalk.

Engraved by Bartolozzi in *Prints . . . from the original pictures and drawings . . . in the Collection of His Majesty*, ii, Pl. 7. The figure of the angel is related to a painting of which two versions are known, one at Chatsworth, as Pietro da Cortona, the other in the Durlacher sale (Christie's, 8.vii.1938, lot 85), as Maratta.

306. THE ANNUNCIATION   (4181)
259 × 214 mm. Red chalk.

Finished studio variant of the original engraving of the composition by Maratta. The poses of the Virgin and the angel differ slightly from the engraving.

307. THE HOLY FAMILY WITH ST. JOHN   (4359)
235 × 171 mm. Red chalk.

Engraved by Bartolozzi after Maratta.

308. THE PENITENT MAGDALEN   (4364 *recto*)
382 × 257 mm. Red chalk, heightened with white, on grey paper. For the *verso* see No. 313 below.

Fig. 47   Cat. No. 311

Perhaps a preliminary study for the composition engraved by Audenaerd. The child's head may be connected with the one of the putti who look down at the Magdalene.

FIGURE OF ST. PETER

309. 249 × 193 mm. Two red chalks.   (4199)

310. 206 × 184 mm. Red chalk.   (4202)

Both studio drawings after a detail of the *Assumption* engraved by Frezza.

311. ST. ANDREW IN GLORY (*Fig. 47*)   (4099)
242 × 191 mm. Pen and bistre. Inscribed: *Carlo Maratti*.

Sketch for the composition engraved from a drawing by P. S. Bartoli after Maratta, dedicated to Cardinal Pietro Ottoboni by Francesco Parteni during the Pontificate of Alexander VIII (1689–91).

312. ST. FRANCIS HOLDING A CRUCIFIX   (4180)
395 × 225 mm. Black chalk over some red chalk.

Engraved by Verkruys. A drawing of the same theme was engraved by Ryland in 1764, when it belonged to the architect Robert Adam.

313. THE CRUCIFIED CHRIST   (4364 *verso*)
382 × 257 mm. Red chalk.

Probably a study for the Christ on the Crucifix held by St. Francis in the above engraved design. Except for a small alteration to the position of the right hand and the addition of a crown of thorns, the engraving follows the drawing almost exactly.

314. STUDY OF DIANA   (4221)

201 × 180 mm. Corners cut off. Red chalk.

Study for the composition of *Pan and Diana* engraved by Frezza after Maratta. The head and shoulders of the goddess only, with the left arm in a different pose from the engraving.

315. WINTER AND SPRING   (01120)

520 × 815 mm. Red chalk. Offset.

A studio drawing after the composition engraved by Audenaerd.

316. ALLEGORY OF DRAWING   (4138)

393 × 267 mm. Black chalk on blue paper.

Studies for a composition engraved by N. Dorigny: two of an *écorché* figure, one after the Farnese Hercules (in reverse); rough sketches of the figure of Leonardo da Vinci pointing to the *écorché* statue and of the man in the right background counting on his fingers.

317. ALLEGORY IN HONOUR OF AN UNKNOWN ROMAN GENTLEMAN (*Plate 51*)   (4091)

414 × 299 mm. Black chalk.

Verso: Study for the figure of Time.

Engraved by Bartolozzi in *Prints . . . from the original pictures and drawings . . . in the Collection of His Majesty*. The engraving shows Time bearing a medallion with the portrait of the hero and trampling on Envy. It is inscribed: CHE L'UOM TRAE DAL SEPOLCRO E A MORTE IL FURA. It has so far proved impossible to identify the person honoured in this drawing, though the profile in the drawing is not unlike that of Carlo Antonio dal Pozzo as shown in a medal, possibly by Gaspero Mola (repr. in Lumbroso, *Notizie della Vita di Cassiano del Pozzo*, Turin, 1875, opp. p. 147). On the other hand, the allusion to Envy does not seem to be particularly relevant to him.

318. ALLEGORY IN HONOUR OF AN UNKNOWN ROMAN GENTLEMAN   (4092)

400 × 271 mm. Black chalk.

Engraved by Bartolozzi in *Prints . . . from the original pictures and drawings . . . in the Collection of His Majesty*. The design, which seems to be planned as a pair to No.317, shows Time seated on a ledge below the oval portrait of a young man and holding an hour-glass. A putto appears to call his attention to the portrait, while another lies asleep in the foreground, beside a palette and brushes.
If No.317 represents Carlo Antonio dal Pozzo, this drawing might be of his son, Ferdinando.
The general idea of the design probably derives from a scheme of Bernini, known from a drawing formerly with Fallani (cf. Brauer and Wittkower, p. 150, and Pl.113a).

319. THE LION OF ST. MARK   (4392)

192 × 261 mm. Red chalk.

Study for the engraving after Maratta by Audenaerd representing the arms of Francesco Morosini (Doge from 1688–94), with allegorical symbols, including the Lion of St.

Mark trampling on symbols of war and the inscription: *Pax tibi Marce.*

320. FRA BONAVENTURA OF BARCELONA (*Plate 61*)   (4366)

250 × 193 mm. Red chalk, with touches of white, on blue paper.

Study for the engraving by G. Colin, reproduced in *Rivista dell' Istituto Nazionale d'Archeologia e Storia dell' Arte*, iv, 1955, p. 292.

3. *Drawings not connected with known works*

321. JUDITH (?)   (4104)

183 × 155 mm. Cut to an Oval. Red chalk, with touches of white, on blue paper.

The figure of a woman holding in her right hand an object cut off by the edge of the paper. The pose suggests Judith with the head of Holofernes. In character the figure is close to the 'Cantemus Domino' engraved by Ferroni in 1705.

322. THE VIRGIN AND CHILD ENTHRONED   (4330)

242 × 223 mm. Red chalk and red wash.

Probably an early drawing in the manner of Sacchi. A drawing in the Albertina (No.786) shows the same theme, but with less fantastic throne. A painting in an anonymous sale at Christie's (25.vii.1958, lot 55), probably after Maratta, shows another variant of the theme.

323. THE VIRGIN AND CHILD ADORED BY ST. MICHAEL AND OTHER SAINTS (*Plate 52*)   (4097)

409 × 263 mm. Red chalk over indications of black chalk.

324. CHRIST HEALING THE SICK   (4146)

271 × 343 mm. Red chalk.

325. THE PENITENT MAGDALEN   (4354)

398 × 262 mm. Red chalk.

326. ST. MARGARET   (4147)

380 × 250 mm. Pen and brown ink, grey wash over red chalk, with touches of white body-colour.

Inscribed: *Carl. Marat . . .* (cut off).

327. ST. JEROME   (4356)

347 × 244 mm. Red chalk.

328. ST. CECILIA   (6097)

328 × 256 mm. Black chalk, with touches of white, on blue paper. Squared.

From the Sassoferrato volumes.

Like No.260 an exact pastiche of Sassoferrato's technique, but unlike him in sentiment. Certainly by the same hand as No.260

329. ST. FRANCIS WITH A ROSARY   (4357)

348 × 248 mm. Red chalk.

330. ST. FRANCIS IN ECSTASY   (4102)

293 × 192 mm. Red chalk.

331. ST. FRANCIS IN PRAYER (4368)

333 × 236 mm. Black chalk with touches of white, on blue paper.

In No.331 the pose of the figure is very close, in reverse, to the *St. Philip Neri* in No.302.

332. THE HEAVENLY HOST (4155)

345 × 228 mm. Red chalk, heightened with white, on blue paper.

Verso: Two heads and a study of drapery.

333. AN ADORING ANGEL (4129)

368 × 240 mm. Red chalk, heightened with white, on grey-green paper.

334. A KNEELING MONK (4174)

273 × 219 mm. Red chalk, with touches of white, on grey-green paper. Numbered: *114*.

Evidently a figure from a larger composition of a vision appearing to the monk.

335. SEATED FIGURE OF A BISHOP (4127)

352 × 251 mm. Black chalk, with touches of white, on grey paper.

336. HEAD OF A BISHOP (4113)

204 × 170 mm. Red chalk, with touches of white, on grey paper.

In the manner of Sacchi, and therefore probably early.

337. ALLEGORY OF SCULPTURE (*Fig. 48*) (4143)

243 × 160 mm. Black chalk, a detail in red chalk.

Perhaps a study for a marble group. On the left a girl chisels a standing figure, while to the right a child holds up what seems to be the drawing from which the sculptress works. A drawing in a rather similar style for the tomb of Innocent XII is in the British Museum.

338. MINERVA (4203)

259 × 188 mm. Red chalk.

Seated figure in armour holding a helmet.

339. VENUS, CUPID AND VULCAN (4358)

211 × 309 mm. Red chalk.

340. LUCRETIA STABBING HERSELF (4121)

233 × 238 mm. Top left corner cut. Black chalk, with touches of white, on grey paper.

341. A SIBYL (4355)

400 × 251 mm. Red chalk.

Adapted from the Libyan Sibyl in the Sistine Chapel.

342. PORTRAIT OF CLEMENT IX (4111)

293 × 203 mm. Red chalk, touches of white.

Fig. 48   Cat. No. 337

The identification of the sitter is based on a drawing of this Pope at Lyons, also attributed to Maratta.

343. PORTRAIT OF A MAN (4216)

238 × 192 mm. Black and red chalk.

Profile portrait of a man with long curly hair.

344. A BEARDED MAN SEATED AND HOLDING A BOOK (?) (4367)

292 × 186 mm. Red chalk.

345. SEATED MALE NUDE, RIGHT LEG RAISED, RIGHT ARM RAISED OVER LEFT SHOULDER (4342)

555 × 413 mm. Red chalk, heightened with white.

346. SEATED MALE NUDE, HIS LEFT HAND ON HIS RIGHT KNEE (4140)

520 × 407 mm. Red chalk, heightened with white.

347. SEATED MALE NUDE, RIGHT LEG AND ARM RAISED (4141)

510 × 407 mm. Red chalk, heightened with white.

348. STANDING MALE NUDE, SEEN FROM BEHIND, BOTH HANDS EXTENDED TO RIGHT (4171)

542 × 358 mm. Red chalk, heightened with white.

349. SEATED MALE NUDE, TO LEFT, HOLDING A TABLET
553 × 409 mm. Red chalk, heightened with white.   (4338)

350. SEATED MALE NUDE, TO LEFT, SEEN FROM BEHIND, HOLDING HIS RAISED RIGHT LEG WITH HIS LEFT HAND
(4339)
508 × 374 mm. Black and white chalk on blue paper. Inscribed in ink: *Carlo Maratti.*

351. SEATED MALE NUDE, RIGHT LEG OVER LEFT, HOLDING A BRANCH IN HIS RIGHT HAND   (4340)
545 × 427 mm. Red chalk, with touches of white. Inscribed in black chalk: *Carlo Maratta.*

352. MALE NUDE, SEATED ON GROUND, SEEN FROM BEHIND   (4341)
382 × 525 mm. Red chalk, heightened with white.

353. TWO HEADS   (4120)
153 × 226 mm. Black chalk, with touches of white, on blue-grey paper.
Heads of a youth and a girl.

354. TWO HEADS   (4219)
224 × 186 mm. Red chalk, with touches of white, on grey-brown paper.
A girl, facing left, with an expression of surprise, and a child looking up.

355. HEAD OF A WOMAN IN PEASANT'S DRESS   (4363)
382 × 258 mm. Red chalk.
A woman wearing the same head-dress appears in a drawing at Frankfort representing a bishop confirming.

356. HEAD OF A GIRL   (4218)
249 × 186 mm. Red chalk.

357. HEAD OF A YOUTH   (4114)
123 × 89 mm. Red chalk, with touches of white, on blue paper.

358. HEAD OF A MAN   (4879)
137 × 88 mm. Red chalk, with touches of white, on blue paper.

359. FOUR HEADS   (4110)
268 × 244 mm. Black chalk, with touches of white, on grey paper.
Two girls, a child, and a veiled head, perhaps a study for the Virgin.

360. HEAD OF A WOMAN   (4106)
353 × 225 mm. Black chalk, heightened with white, on grey paper.
Perhaps a portrait.

361. HEAD AND HAND OF A WOMAN   (4107)
346 × 226 mm. Red chalk on blue paper.

362. HEAD OF A WOMAN   (4116)
167 × 115 mm. Black chalk, with touches of white, on blue-grey paper.
Faint indications of a halo.

363. HEAD OF A GIRL IN A TURBAN   (4213)
217 × 177 mm. Red chalk.
Heads of a similar type appear in the *Judith* engraved by Ferroni, and the *Rebecca and Eliezer* engraved by Audenaerd.

364. HEAD OF A WOMAN   (4115)
124 × 100 mm. Cut to an oval. Red chalk on blue paper.

365. HEAD OF A WOMAN   (4160)
90 × 86 mm. Red chalk.
Profile head with a scarf wrapped round the hair.

366. BUST OF A WOMAN   (4228)
179 × 175 mm. Red chalk.

367. HEAD OF A BOY   (4119)
206 × 184 mm. Black chalk on grey-brown paper.

HEADS OF BABIES

368. 230 × 92 mm. Black chalk. On two separate pieces of pink prepared paper.   (5170)
Without traditional attribution, but certainly by Maratta.

369. 197 × 192 mm. Black chalk, with touches of white, on grey paper.   (4109)

370. SHEET OF STUDIES   (4131)
371 × 250 mm. Red chalk on grey-brown paper.
A head of a youth, three hands, and indications of a figure reading.

371. A DOG   (4139)
185 × 249 mm. Red chalk.

372. HEAD OF A LION   (4394)
295 × 209 mm. Black and white chalk on grey paper.

4. Drawings after the Antique
THE APOLLO BELVEDERE
In the Vatican.

373. THE WHOLE STATUE   (4380)
287 × 186 mm. Red chalk.
Studio drawing.

374. DRAWING OF THE HEAD   (4117)
184 × 134 mm. Black chalk, touches of white, on grey-brown paper.

MARCUS AURELIUS SACRIFICING BEFORE THE TEMPLE OF JUPITER
Relief in the Palazzo dei Conservatori.

375. THE WHOLE RELIEF   (4373)
257 × 184 mm. Black chalk.

376. THE FIGURES ONLY   (4374)

212 × 271 mm. Black chalk, heightened with white, on grey-brown paper.

THE SACRIFICE OF A BULL

Bas-relief formerly in the Villa Medici, now in the Uffizi.

377. 207 × 203 mm. Black chalk.   (4372)

THE FARNESE FLORA

Formerly in the Palazzo Farnese, now in Naples.

378. SEEN FROM THE FRONT   (4377)

294 × 159 mm. Black chalk.

379. SEEN FROM THE SIDE   (4383)

285 × 159 mm. Black chalk.

THE FARNESE HERCULES

Formerly in the Palazzo Farnese, now in Naples.

380. SEEN FROM THE FRONT   (4382)

292 × 165 mm. Red chalk.

381. SEEN FROM BEHIND   (4384)

252 × 154 mm. Red chalk.
Two studio drawings.

BACCHUS

From the Borghese collection (cf. Perrier, *Segmenta*, Pl. 47).

382. 293 × 158 mm. Black chalk.   (4378)

RELIEF OF MARCUS AURELIUS

In the Capitoline Museum.

383. FIGURE OF A SOLDIER   (4386)

262 × 172 mm. Red chalk.

A MUSE

In the Capitoline Museum (cf. Perrier, *Segmenta*, Pl. 74).

384. 293 × 140 mm. Black chalk, heightened with white, on light-brown tinted paper.   (4379)

STATUE OF LUCIUS VERUS

In the Naples Gallery.

385. DRAWING OF THE TORSO   (4387)

202 × 168 mm. Black chalk.

MAENAD

From a sarcophagus in the Villa Albani (Reinach, *Rép. Rel.*, iii, p. 143, No.1).

386. 245 × 168 mm. Red chalk.   (4381)

NOVA NUPTA

Formerly in the Palazzo della Valle (engraved in P. S. Bartoli, *Admiranda Vestigia*, Pl. 59).

387. 164 × 206 mm. Black chalk.   (4371)

388. HEAD OF (THE CAETANI?) APHRODITE   (4108)

192 × 135 mm. One corner torn and patched. Red chalk, with touches of white, on blue paper.

389. HEAD OF THE CAPITOLINE HOMER   (4112)

183 × 134 mm. Black chalk on grey paper.

A DRAPED TORSO

390. 220 × 170 mm. Black chalk.   (4388)

391. 294 × 200 mm. Red chalk, with red wash. (4389)

Two studies of the same fragment. Like the Giustiniani Septimius Severus, now at Williams College, Mass. (See also No. 777.)

392. PUTTO, ACANTHUS AND CANDELABRUM   (4269)

178 × 174 mm. Black chalk.

Fragments from the Domus Flavia or the Forum Traiani (Reinach, *op. cit.*, iii, p. 287, No. 5.

Two further drawings after the Antique from the Maratta volumes, evidently not by him, have been catalogued among the sixteenth-century drawings (cf. Popham and Wilde, Nos. 1145, 1146).

5. Drawings after other masters

AFTER RAPHAEL

From Bellori's life of Maratta (*Vite di Guido Reni, Andrea Sacchi e Carlo Maratti*, ed. M. Piacentini, Rome, 1942, pp. 75, 76, 114 ff., 143 ff.) we know that throughout his life the artist constantly copied the works of Raphael, and that he preserved some of his early copies in a volume. This volume probably contained the bulk of the drawings at Windsor after Raphael, since many of them are very highly finished and therefore probably early in date. A few, however, are in the more vigorous later style. Some may be connected with the restoration of the Stanze which Maratta undertook for Clement XI in 1702–3 (*ibid.* p. 108), particularly the drawings after the caryatids in the Stanza d'Eliodoro, which show them with their lower halves damaged, in which state, according to Bellori, they were when Maratta undertook the work. Most of the drawings appear to be by Maratta himself, but since their interest lies in their relation to Raphael rather than in the light they throw on the style of Maratta, no attempt has been made to sort out those which might be by skilful members of the studio. On the other hand, the volume also contained a number of other drawings connected with Raphael (including one original) but quite unconnected with Maratta or his circle. These have been catalogued in the section dealing with Raphael in Popham and Wilde's catalogue of the Italian drawings of the fifteenth and sixteenth centuries (Nos. 818 and 835–847).

STANZA DELLA SEGNATURA
THE SCHOOL OF ATHENS

393. TWO FIGURES (4252)
230 × 193 mm. Red chalk. On two pieces of paper joined.

394. TWO FIGURES (4253)
213 × 157 mm. Red chalk.

395. ONE FIGURE (4254)
293 × 148 mm. Red and black chalk.

396. ONE FIGURE (4255)
236 × 182 mm. Red chalk.

397. HEAD OF AN OLD MAN (4256)
207 × 158 mm. Red chalk.

398. HEAD OF A BOY (4258)
215 × 199 mm. Red chalk.

399. HEAD OF A GIRL (4259)
228 × 186 mm. Red chalks.

400. HEAD OF A MAN WEARING A HELMET (4260)
252 × 184 mm. Red chalk.

THE DISPUTA

401. SEATED OLD MAN (4243)
235 × 197 mm. Red chalk.

402. STANDING FIGURE (4244)
244 × 190 mm. Red chalk.

403. SEATED WOMAN (4245)
231 × 184 mm. Red chalk.

404. SEATED WOMAN, WRITING (4251)
211 × 186 mm. Red chalk.

405. HEAD OF A MAN IN PROFILE TO LEFT (4247)
210 × 150 mm. Red chalk.

406. HEAD AND SHOULDERS OF A MAN, IN FEIGNED OVAL (4248)
190 × 192 mm. Red chalks.

407. HEAD OF A BISHOP, TO RIGHT (4249)
238 × 179 mm. Red chalks.

408. HEADS OF TWO WOMEN (4250)
205 × 198 mm. Red chalks.

409. HEAD OF DANTE (4265)
229 × 150 mm. Red chalk.

JUSTICE

410. FIGURE OF PRUDENCE (4239)
189 × 218 mm. Red chalks.

411. FIGURE OF FORTITUDE (4240)
185 × 210 mm. Red chalks.

412. FIGURE OF TEMPERANCE (4241)
201 × 207 mm. Red chalk.

GREGORY IX HANDING OVER
THE DECRETALIA

413. HEAD AND SHOULDERS OF AN OLD MAN (4266)
227 × 168 mm. Red chalk.

THE JUDGMENT OF SOLOMON

414. WOMAN KNEELING AT THE FOOT OF ANOTHER FIGURE (4262)
261 × 168 mm. Red chalks.

STANZA D'ELIODORO
THE MASS OF BOLSENA

415. SEATED WOMAN AND CHILD (4315)
202 × 201 mm. Red chalk.

416. HEAD OF A MAN (4324)
220 × 153 mm. Red chalks.
Reversed; probably an offset.

THE DADO

417. THE TIBER (4237)
219 × 406 mm. Red chalks.

418. ABUNDANCE (4238)
214 × 398 mm. Red chalk, heightened with white.

419. FIGURE DRINKING (4201)
259 × 161 mm. Red chalk.
From the grisaille representing *Harvest* painted by Maratta.

420. A CARYATID (4233)
266 × 181 mm. Red chalk.

421. A CARYATID (4234)
264 × 135 mm. Red chalk.

422. A CARYATID (4235)
272 × 175 mm. Red chalk.

423. A CARYATID WITH AN ANCHOR (4236)
270 × 183 mm. Red chalk.

424. A CARYATID (4319)
256 × 180 mm. Red chalk. Unfinished.

THE CEILING

425. GOD APPEARING TO NOAH   (4263)
179 × 255 mm. Red chalk.

426. SACRIFICE OF ABRAHAM   (4264)
188 × 191 mm. Red chalk.

STANZA DELL' INCENDIO
THE VICTORY OF OSTIA

427. SANDALS AND A HELMET   (4314)
276 × 141 mm. Red chalk.

THE CORONATION OF CHARLEMAGNE

428. HEAD IN PROFILE TO LEFT   (4246)
228 × 186 mm. Red chalk.

STANZA DI COSTANTINO

429. ENERGY, AND POPE FELIX III   (4229)
538 × 366 mm. Red chalk.

430. TEMPERANCE   (4230)
430 × 256 mm. Red chalk.

431. JUSTICE   (4231)
440 × 301 mm. Red chalk.

432. RELIGION   (4232)
549 × 404 mm. Red chalk.

433. FIGURE OF A GIRL   (4317)
258 × 162 mm. Red chalk.

434. FIGURE OF A MAN   (4318)
258 × 176 mm. Red chalk.

CONSTANTINE ADDRESSING HIS ARMY

435. STUDIES OF HELMETS, SANDALS AND A STANDING
FIGURE   (4316)
282 × 205 mm. Red chalk.

THE LOGGIE

436. MOSES GIVING THE LAW   (4292)
193 × 213 mm. Red chalk.

437. HEAD OF A WOMAN   (4210)
214 × 155 mm. Red chalk.
Probably from the *Crossing of the Red Sea*.

438. A WINGED FIGURE SEATED ON A GLOBE   (4186)
289 × 211 mm. Red chalk.

THE FARNESINA

439. GALATEA   (4323)
392 × 294 mm. Red chalk.

PSYCHE RECEIVED INTO OLYMPUS

440. SEATED WOMAN   (4242)
250 × 162 mm. Red chalk.

441. RECLINING MALE NUDE   (4385)
176 × 275 mm. Red chalks.

442. HEAD OF BACCHUS   (4214)
176 × 134 mm. Red chalk.

443. HEAD OF A YOUNG WARRIOR   (4257)
217 × 153 mm. Red chalk.

THE MARRIAGE OF CUPID AND PSYCHE

444. FEMALE FIGURE HOLDING A WREATH   (4325)
207 × 194 mm. Red chalk.

SPANDREL

445. HEAD OF VENUS   (4215)
155 × 134 mm. Red chalk.

SISTINE CHAPEL TAPESTRIES

446. THE MIRACULOUS DRAUGHT   (4296)
237 × 298 mm. Red chalk.

447. THE CONVERSION OF SAUL   (4297)
225 × 350 mm. Red chalks.

448. THE DEATH OF ANANIAS   (4298)
199 × 333 mm. Red chalks.

449. ST. PAUL AT ATHENS   (4304)
230 × 307 mm. Red chalk.

450. THE CHARGE TO ST. PETER   (4305)
229 × 337 mm. Red chalks.

451. THE SACRIFICE AT LYSTRA
245 × 189 mm. Red chalk. Left part. Unfinished.   (4312)

452. TWO KNEELING FIGURES   (4303)
443 × 300 mm. Red chalk.

453. ST. PAUL   (4313)
226 × 122 mm. Red chalk.

SCUOLA NUOVA TAPESTRIES
THE ADORATION OF THE MAGI

454. A STANDING MAN, AND HEAD OF ANOTHER   (4299)
294 × 193 mm. Red chalk.

455. A GROUP OF ADORING FIGURES   (4307)
192 × 292 mm. Red chalk.

456. A CROUCHING FIGURE   (4308)
241 × 200 mm. Red chalk.

457. A BEARDED HEAD, PROFILE TO LEFT   (4301)
246 × 186 mm. Red chalk.

458. A BEARDED HEAD IN A CAP   (4302)
264 × 183 mm. Red chalk.

THE PRESENTATION

459. ATTENDANTS BEARING GIFTS   (4309)
292 × 201 mm. Red chalk.

460. THE VIRGIN AND CHILD   (4310)
308 × 179 mm. Red chalk. Unfinished.

461. TWO STANDING WOMEN   (4311)
309 × 181 mm. Red chalk.

462. STUDIES OF THREE HEADS AND TWO FEET   (4300)
266 × 188 mm. Red chalk.

THE RESURRECTION

463. TWO KNEELING FIGURES, TO LEFT   (4306)
341 × 317 mm. Red chalk.

464. STUDIES OF ARMOUR   (4321)
227 × 358 mm. Black chalk.

PAINTINGS
FAITH, HOPE AND CHARITY (Vatican Gallery)

465. CHARITY   (4331)
213 × 203 mm. In circular frame. Red chalk.

466. FAITH   (4332)
217 × 192 mm. In circular frame. Red chalks.

467. HOPE   (4333)
199 × 193 mm. In circular frame. Red chalks.

THE TRANSFIGURATION (Vatican Gallery)

468. HEAD OF A WOMAN, PROFILE TO LEFT   (4267)
336 × 249 mm. Red chalk.

469. HEAD OF A BEARDED MAN   (4268)
338 × 235 mm. Red chalk.

HOLY FAMILY (Louvre)

470. MADONNA AND CHILD   (4327)
249 × 196 mm. Red chalk. Unfinished.

AFTER MICHELANGELO
THE CREATION OF SUN AND MOON
(Vatican, Sistine Chapel)

471. STUDY OF THE FIGURE ON THE LEFT   (4261)
295 × 278 mm. Red chalk.

472. STUDY OF THE GROUP ON THE RIGHT   (4281)
186 × 287 mm. Red chalk.

TOMB OF JULIUS II
(S. Pietro in Montorio, Rome)

473. DRAWING AFTER THE FIGURE OF LEAH   (4196)
252 × 186 mm. Red chalk.

One drawing after Michelangelo from the Maratta volumes, but not by him, has been catalogued in the volume dealing with sixteenth-century masters (Popham and Wilde, No.484).

AFTER CORREGGIO
Parma, Cathedral

474. VARIOUS FIGURES FROM THE DOME   (4273)
201 × 295 mm. Red chalk, heightened with white.

475. TWO FIGURES FROM THE DOME   (4272)
257 × 189 mm. Red chalk, heightened with white.

476. PUTTI FROM THE DOME   (4274)
230 × 325 mm. Red chalk, with touches of white.

477. TWO ANGELS FROM THE DOME   (4276)
260 × 193 mm. Red chalk, heightened with white.

478. NUDE FIGURE FROM ONE OF THE PENDENTIVES
260 × 193 mm. Red chalk, heightened with white.   (4275)
All studio drawings.

AFTER POLIDORO DA CARAVAGGIO
SATURN DEVOURING HIS CHILDREN

Fresco formerly on the façade of a Palazzo in the Via della Maschera d'Oro.

479. COPY OF THE WHOLE COMPOSITION   (4329)
253 × 129 mm. Red chalk.
Probably a studio drawing.

480. JANUS   (4328)
284 × 177 mm. Red chalk and red wash.

A copy after a lost drawing by Polidoro da Caravaggio of which other copies are known (*e.g.* in Berlin and in the British Museum). Maratta probably used this drawing as the basis for the Janus in the painting of *Winter and Spring* engraved by Audenaerd (cf. No.315).

AFTER ANNIBALE CARRACCI
Rome, S. Giacomo degli Spagnuoli, Cappella S. Diego

481. KNEELING FIGURE   (4187)
274 × 193 mm. Red chalk.
The right-hand figure in the *Invocation of S. Diego*.

482. A PUTTO   (4205)
189 × 202 mm. In feigned oval. Red chalks.
From the fresco of *God the Father*.

483. A HEAD, A KNEE, AND A FOOT (4212)
247 × 184 mm. Red chalks.
The head is of St. James, the foot of St. John the Baptist, and the knee of God the Father.
Probably all studio drawings.

ROME, Palazzo Farnese, Gallery

484. DETAILS OF THE DECORATION (4393)
280 × 148 mm. Red chalks on white paper.
For a copy of the same motive by Domenichino, cf. Pope-Hennessy, *The Drawings of Domenichino at Windsor Castle*, No.1755.

AFTER GUIDO RENI
LENINGRAD, Hermitage

485. THE VIRGIN SEWING (3248)
See Kurz, *Bolognese Drawings*, No.378.

ROME, S. Gregorio al Celio
CHOIR OF ANGELS

486. HEAD OF AN ANGEL (4208)
257 × 194 mm. Red chalk, heightened with white, on white paper.

487. HEAD AND SHOULDERS OF AN ANGEL (4209)
279 × 198 mm. Red chalk, heightened with white, on white paper.

Formerly ROME, Montecitorio
BACCHUS AND ARIADNE

488. A PUTTO (4197)
177 × 248 mm. Red chalk.
Probably an offset.

AFTER DOMENICHINO
GROTTAFERRATA, Abbey
THE LIFE OF S. NILO

489. AN ANGEL, SUPPORTING AN OVAL FRAME TO LEFT
261 × 188 mm. Red chalk. (4188)

490. AN ANGEL, SUPPORTING AN OVAL FRAME TO RIGHT
270 × 185 mm. Red chalk. (4190)

491. GOD THE FATHER (4193)
230 × 193 mm. Red chalk.

ROME, S. Gregorio al Celio
THE FLAGELLATION OF ST. ANDREW

492. COPY OF THE WHOLE COMPOSITION (4271)
281 × 445 mm. Fine red and black chalk on white paper, incised.
Perhaps the drawing mentioned in the inventory of Maratta's possessions (cf. *L'Archiginnasio*, Bologna, xxii, 1927, p. 234, No.48).

ROME, S. Maria della Vittoria
THE VIRGIN AND CHILD
WITH ST. FRANCIS
Reproduced in J. Pope-Hennessy, *The Drawings of Domenichino at Windsor Castle*, p. 88, Fig. 45.

493. COPY OF THE FIGURE OF THE VIRGIN (4277)
260 × 155 mm. Red chalk.

494. TWO PUTTI (4226)
255 × 174 mm. Red chalk on white paper.
The originals cannot be traced in Domenichino's paintings, but their type suggests that they may be after a lost work by him. Studio drawing.

AFTER ANDREA SACCHI
ALTHORP, Earl Spencer Collection
APOLLO CROWNING THE SINGER
PASQUALINI
The painting is reproduced from an engraving in Posse, p. 110. It was originally in the Palazzo Pallavicini (cf. E. Wright, *Some observations made in travelling through France, Italy . . .*, London, 1730, i, p. 295).

495. COPY OF THE WHOLE COMPOSITION (6838)
549 × 410 mm. Red chalk.
Inscribed: *Disegno del S. Cav^e Maratta copiato da un quadro d'Andrea Sacchi*.
Inv. A, p. 125: 'Apollo rewarding Merit (A Copy by Carlo Maratti from his Master Andrea Sacchi).

AFTER RIBERA
NAPLES, Certosa di S. Martino
THE VIRGIN LAMENTING
THE DEAD CHRIST

496. COPY OF THE WHOLE COMPOSITION (4153)
461 × 329 mm. Red chalk.
An offset.

CARLO MARATTA (attributed to)

497. HEAD OF A MAN (4880)
234 × 181 mm. Red chalk.
From the Sacchi volumes.

498. HEAD OF A BOY (5148)
208 × 175 mm. Red chalk on blue paper.

499. HEAD OF A WOMAN (5392)
144 × 115 mm. Upper corners cut off. Red chalk on blue paper.

CARLO MARATTA (after)

500. JOSEPH AND POTIPHAR'S WIFE (5651)
305 × 235 mm. Black chalk.

Inv. A, p. 110, as Pietro de Pietri.

Probably a copy by Pietro de Pietri after Maratta's drawing for the composition engraved in reverse by Ferroni. A copy by Ferroni, perhaps for the engraving, is in the Albertina (No.780).

501. MATER DOLOROSA (4407)

205 × 168 mm. Red chalk.

Inv. A, p. 110: From the volume containing drawings by Passeri, Pietro de Pietri and Masucci.

An exact copy of the composition by Maratta engraved by Bartolomeus de Petri. Perhaps by Pietro de Pietri.

502. HEAD OF THE MADONNA (4207)

254 × 199 mm. Red chalk.

Probably after a painting.

503. STUDIES OF HEADS, ETC. (4224)

218 × 193 mm. Red chalk.

By the same hand as No.508.

CARLO MARATTA (studio of)

504. HEAD OF THE MADONNA (4158)

216 × 169 mm. Black chalk.

Studio copy. Offset.

505. HEAD OF THE MADONNA (6051)

309 × 249 mm. Red chalk.

From the Sassoferrato volumes, but quite unlike him in style. Probably for an engraving.

506. CHRIST IN THE GARDEN, SURROUNDED BY PUTTI CARRYING THE SYMBOLS OF THE PASSION (4090)

421 × 290 mm. Red chalk.

507. ALLEGORY OF WISDOM (4204)

255 × 175 mm. Red chalk.

The figure of a woman holding a snake and a looking-glass.

508. ALLEGORICAL FIGURE (4189)

269 × 182 mm. Red chalk.

A figure running and holding a palm.

509. ALLEGORICAL FIGURE (4200)

227 × 182 mm. Red chalk.

Studio drawings after Maratta or some other master.

510. SHEET OF STUDIES (4191)

193 × 262 mm. Red chalk.

A woman carrying a water pot, a woman wearing a veil, a head of a youth, and a fragment of drapery.

511. FIGURE OF A MAN (4322)

268 × 156 mm. Red chalk.

512. AN OLD MAN WITH HIS HANDS CLASPED (4278)

264 × 187 mm. Red chalk.

513. HEAD OF A GIRL (298)

393 × 243 mm. Red chalk.

From the Domenichino volumes.

514. A BEARDED FIGURE (4270)

273 × 161 mm. Red chalk.

Probably after a painting, perhaps an offset.

515. HEAD OF A BEARDED MAN (4192)

252 × 174 mm. Red chalk.

Probably after a painting.

516. HEAD OF A PUTTO (4225)

253 × 159 mm. Red chalk.

Probably after a painting.

517. A FLYING FIGURE (4198)

270 × 192 mm. Red chalk.

Probably after a painting.

518. SHEET OF STUDIES (4220)

249 × 186 mm. Red chalk.

A head and sketches of trees.

CARLO MARATTA (followers of)

519. THE HOLY FAMILY (4361)

203 × 155 mm. Red chalk.

520. THE VIRGIN, CHILD AND S. ANNE ADORED BY TWO MONKS (4426)

226 × 185 mm. Red chalk.

Inv. A, p. 110: 'Pietro de Petris, Masucci and other Scholars of Carlo Maratti.'

521. THE VIRGIN AND CHILD (1768)

315 × 218 mm. Red chalk.

From the Carracci volumes.

Probably an offset.

522. THE VIRGIN AND CHILD WITH ST. JOHN (4167)

250 × 306 mm. Oval. Red chalk on grey-green paper.

523. THE VIRGIN AND CHILD ADORED BY A HERMIT (6775)

139 × 100 mm. Pen and brown ink, with brown and black wash, on paper prepared with blue wash.

The connection with Maratta is somewhat tenuous, but the kneeling hermit is close in type to certain of his figures, such as the *Elijah* (cf. No.296).

524. ST. JEROME (5644)

189 × 189 mm. Red chalk.

Inv. A, p. 110, as Pietro de Pietri.

Not apparently by any of the identifiable followers of Maratta, though nearest in style to Masucci.

525. THE VIRGIN IN GLORY ADORED BY TWO SAINTS
245 × 153 mm. Black chalk.   (4362)

526. MEDOR AND ANGELICA   (5647)
191 × 257 mm. Red chalk.

Inv. A, p. 110, as Pietro de Pietri.

The drawing does not seem to conform exactly to the style of Pietro de Pietri, Masucci, or Stefano Pozzo, but is certainly by a close and competent follower of Maratta.

527. ALLEGORY OF PLENTY OR FORTUNE   (4176)
208 × 397 mm. Black chalk on grey-blue paper.

A group of men and women approach a figure who pours out the contents of a cornucopia. On one side stands Mercury, on the other a priest.

528. PORTRAIT OF A MAN IN A WIG   (5186)
198 × 155 mm. Black, red and white chalk, on grey-brown paper.

Related to Maratta's type of painted portrait, but probably by Jacob Ferdinand Voet, who practised this manner in Rome in the 1660's and 1670's. The closest parallel is a portrait of a Pompeo Rocci in the Spada Gallery (cf. F. Zeri, *La Galleria Spada in Roma*, Florence, 1954, p. 147, No. 12, and Fig. 205).

529. HEAD OF A BEARDED MAN   (5380)
207 × 205 mm. Red chalk. Undecipherable collector's mark.
Inv. A, p. 19, as School of the Carracci.

530. HEAD OF A WOMAN   (5393)
127 × 137 mm. Red chalk.

531. HEAD OF A CHILD   (4416)
121 × 97 mm. Black chalk with touches of white, on grey-green paper.

532. A MAN WIELDING A SWORD   (7707)
240 × c.160 mm. Black chalk.
On the back of an engraving.

AGOSTINO MASUCCI
(c.1691–1758)

533. HEAD OF A BEARDED MAN (*Fig. 49*)   (4404)
343 × 267 mm. Black, red and white chalk on grey paper.

Inv. A, p. 110: from a group of ten drawings ascribed to Pietro di Pietri.

Perhaps a study for the head of Christ.

In spite of the old attribution to Pietro di Pietri this drawing and the next differ so markedly from those certainly by him, and are so much closer to drawings attributed to Masucci, that the old attribution cannot be maintained.

Fig. 49   Cat. No. 533

534. HEAD OF AN ECCLESIASTIC   (4403)
407 × 308 mm. Black, white and red chalk on grey paper.

From the same group as No. 533, but to be ascribed to Masucci for the same reason.

535. A SEATED MALE NUDE   (0257)
459 × 283 mm. Red and white chalk on blue paper.

The old mount had the name of Masucci on it. Probably Inventory A, p. 147, No. 48, as Masucci.

GIOVANNI PAOLO MELCHIORI
(1664–1745)
(attributed to)

536. A PRIEST IN PRAYER BEFORE A SKULL AND A CRUCIFIX (4427)
414 × 270 mm. Black and white chalk on grey-green paper.

Inv. A, p. 110: from a volume containing Pietro di Pietri, Masucci, and other followers of Maratta.

Close in general character, but not in detail, to a composition of *St. Peter Celestinus*, engraved by Fariat after Melchiori.

537. A STANDING MALE NUDE   (0209)
408 × 265 mm. Black and white chalk on blue-grey paper.

The old mount had the name of Melchiori. Probably Inventory A, p. 147, No. 47, as Melchiori.

PIER FRANCESCO MOLA
(1612–66)

Many drawings attributed to Mola exist in the private and public collections of Europe, but the basis for their association with his name is not always clear, although most of them represent the equivalent in drawing to the mixture of Roman and Venetian elements which are to be found in his paintings.

One of the following drawings, the *Bacchus and Ariadne* (No.538), is of importance in that it is a preparation for a known painting and shows a marked style with loose pen drawing and free, rich use of wash. One of the few other drawings which can be connected with a painting—the *Joseph before his Brethren* in the British Museum (1853–10–8–10), which is for a painting in the Quirinal—has the same technique which is also to be found in the *Expulsion* from the Fenwick collection, also in the British Museum, which comes ultimately from Resta and Somers.

The other drawings at Windsor are different in manner. *St. John in the Wilderness* (No.542), in pen only, is like Mola's paintings of this subject in composition. Three others (Nos.539, 540, 541) have the combination of red chalk with brown pen and wash which is often found in drawings called Mola and are also drawn with a very thick pen, probably a reed, associated with this group. The reed-pen allows of unusual variations in the thickness of the stroke, a feature which seems to be characteristic of Mola's style. It is also to be found in certain landscape drawings at Windsor, which are for this reason attributed to him, but with considerable reservations, since they also bear a resemblance to the style of Testa.

538. BACCHUS AND ARIADNE (*Fig. 50*)   (6799)

200 × 261 mm. Pen and brown wash over red and black chalk. Inscribed on the mount: *F. Mola dipinsse del Palazzo Costaguti.*

Fig. 50   Cat. No. 538

Fig. 51   Cat. No. 545

A study for the ceiling fresco executed c.1657 (repr. *Bollettino d'Arte*, viii, 1928, p. 67). An unusual drawing for Mola, but very close to one of the *Expulsion* from the Fenwick collection, now in the British Museum.

539. THE HOLY FAMILY (*Plate 42*)   (6776)

108 × 139 mm. In an octagonal frame. Pen and brown ink over red chalk.

540. A WOMAN WITH A UNICORN   (6798)

151 × 131 mm. Pen and brown wash over red chalk.

Freely based on the figures at the bottom of Domenichino's pendentive fresco of *Temperance* in S. Carlo ai Catinari.

541. VENUS FINDING THE DEAD ADONIS (*Plate 41*) (3598)

141 × 179 mm. Pen and brown ink. Two figures in red chalk, not connected with the main group, and some red chalk rubbed off another drawing.

From the volumes of *Bolognesi Moderni*.

542. ST. JOHN THE BAPTIST IN THE WILDERNESS (6766)

198 × 236 mm. Pen and brown ink. Torn and mended.

543. LANDSCAPE WITH A HERMIT   (6162)

195 × 260 mm. Pen and brown ink.

544. WOODED LANDSCAPE   (0831)

281 × 418 mm. Pen and brown ink.

545. LANDSCAPE WITH FIGURES (*Fig. 51*)   (6151)

267 × 406 mm. Pen and brown wash.

Apparently Inv. A, p. 115: as Grimaldi.

546. LANDSCAPE WITH FIGURES BESIDE A STREAM (*Plate 40*)   (0830)

265 × 210 mm. Pen and brown ink. Stained.

547. HEAD OF A BEARDED MAN   (5377)

182 × 149 mm. Oval. Black, red and white chalk. Torn and mended. Inscribed on the mount: *F. Mola.*

The attribution is based solely on the old inscription, since there are no similar drawings by Mola available for comparison.

PIER FRANCESCO MOLA
(attributed to)

548. LANDSCAPE WITH TOBIAS AND THE ANGEL (1504)
178 × 259 mm. Pen and brown ink.
From the Domenichino volumes, but much closer to the penmanship of Mola.

549. STUDIES OF THE VIRGIN AND CHILD (6785)
138 × 76 mm. Pen and brown ink over red chalk.
Two studies for the Virgin holding the Child, with a sketch of trees above. The attribution to Mola is based on the similarity with a drawing of the *Flight into Egypt* in the British Museum (1895-9-15-714).

550. TREES IN A WOOD, A STEEP HILL IN THE DISTANCE (5805)
265 × 301 mm. Pen and brown ink, brown washes, over faint black chalk indications.
The tentative attribution to Mola is based on the similarity to No.545.

CRESCENZIO DEGLI ONOFRI
(1632-98)

So little is known for certain of either the paintings or the drawings of this artist that it is difficult to do more than put under his name those drawings which have old attributions, and those which seem to have a close affinity to them or to others ascribed to him in other collections.

551. LANDSCAPE WITH A VILLA (*Fig. 52*) (6136)
233 × 413 mm. Pen and brown wash over black chalk.
The attribution was written on the old mount.

552. LANDSCAPE WITH A TOWN BY A RIVER (*Fig. 53*) (6135)
232 × 378 mm. Pen and brown wash, heightened with white, on grey paper.
The old mount had the name of Onofri.

553. LANDSCAPE WITH A RIVER (3539)
205 × 293 mm. Pen and brown ink on white paper, now discoloured. Inscribed on the mount: *Cres: de Onofri.*
A closely similar drawing ascribed to Onofri at Besançon (No.3007) confirms the traditional attribution.

554. HILLY LANDSCAPE WITH A VILLA AND A HUNTSMAN SHOOTING WATER-FOWL (3538)
201 × 291 mm. Pen and brown ink on white paper, much darkened. Inscribed on the mount: *Cres: de Onofri.*

555. WOODED LANDSCAPE WITH A RIVER AND A BOAT (6161)
198 × 266 mm. Pen and brown ink.

556. LANDSCAPE WITH A CASTELLO (6159)
362 × 466 mm. Pen and brown ink.

Fig. 52   Cat. No. 551

Fig. 53   Cat. No. 552

CRESCENZIO DEGLI ONOFRI
(attributed to)

557. LANDSCAPE WITH FIGURES   (5728)

419 × 283 mm. Pen and brown ink with grey wash.
Similar in technique and style to No.552.

ORLANDI (attributed to)

558. PORTRAIT OF A MAN   (5176)

147 × 111 mm. Pen and brown ink over red chalk, with
water-colour. Damaged and faded.

559. PORTRAIT OF A WOMAN   (5177)

147 × 111 mm. Pen and brown ink over red chalk, with
water-colour. Damaged and faded.

No.559 had on its old mount the inscription *ORLANDI PITTRICE*

MINIATURA, which may refer either to the sitter or to the artist,
but no paintress of this name seems to be recorded. The
drawings are broadly speaking in the manner of Leoni.

GIOVANNI PAOLO PANNINI
(1691–1765)

560. FOUR STUDIES OF RUNNING FOOTMEN (*Fig. 54*)
                                                (13107)

190 × 300 mm. Red chalk. Inscribed: *Watteau*.

Verso: Studies of a servant and a spectator.

Lit.: C. Stuart Wortley, *Old Master Drawings*, xi, 1936, p. 45
(with reproductions of a detail of the painting (p. 45) and of
the drawing (Pls. 41, 42)).

Studies for the painting of *The Duc de Choiseul leaving the
Vatican*, executed in 1756, in the collection of the Earl of
Ellesmere.

Fig. 54   Cat. No. 560

GIOVANNI PAOLO PANNINI
(attributed to)

561. RUINS WITH FIGURES (7706)

302 × 241 mm. Pen and grey wash over black chalk.
Collector's mark: Paul Sandby. Bought in 1944.

GIOVANNI PAOLO PANNINI
(follower of)

VIEWS OF RUINS

562. 273 × 366 mm. Pen and dark brown ink, touched with body-colour, on grey-brown paper. (10770)

563. 268 × 367 mm. Pen and dark brown ink, touched with body-colour, on grey-brown paper. (10771)

These two drawings are by the same feeble imitator of Pannini.

ROMAN RUINS WITH FIGURES

564. 222 × 268 mm. Pen and light brown wash, heightened with body-colour, on buff paper. (10772)

565. 226 × 272 mm. Pen and light brown wash, heightened with body-colour, on buff paper. (10773)

These two drawings are of better quality than Nos.562 and 563 and near to Pannini himself.

GIUSEPPE PASSERI
(1654–1714)

All the following drawings, except three (Nos.566, 582 and 587), come from a series attributed to Passeri in Inventory A, and eight of them are for paintings known to be by him. His highly characteristic style, with its unusual technique, combining red chalk, pen and brown wash, with white or white and grey gouache, confirms the attribution of the remaining drawings and seems to justify the addition of the three from other volumes.

1. Drawings connected with known works

Formerly BERLIN, Lanz Collection
CHRIST DRIVING THE MONEY-CHANGERS OUT OF THE TEMPLE

Sold Hecht, Charlottenburg, 14.v.1928, lot 261; attributed to Passeri by Voss.

566. STUDY FOR THE WHOLE COMPOSITION (*Fig. 55*) (4502)

273 × 382 mm. Pen and brown wash, heightened with white and grey gouache over red chalk.

The drawing agrees almost exactly with the painting.

Another drawing for the same painting is at Düsseldorf (No.408).

Fig. 55   Cat. No. 566

Fig. 56   Cat. No. 568

DIJON, Museum
ST. BERNARD RECEIVED INTO CITEAUX BY ST. STEPHEN

The painting comes from the Abbey of Cîteaux and was a pendant to the *Cessation of the Schism of Anacletus*, hitherto also attributed to Passeri, but probably by Pietro di Pietri (cf. No.667).

567. STUDY FOR THE WHOLE COMPOSITION   (01231)

513 × 397 mm. Pen and brown wash, heightened with white over red chalk.

This drawing agrees exactly with the painting. but is in reverse.

FLORENCE, Private Collection
MADONNA OF THE ROSARY

Reproduced Voss, p. 359.

568. STUDY FOR THE WHOLE COMPOSITION (*Fig. 56*)
                                 (0270)

219 × 143 mm. Pen and brown wash, heightened with white and grey gouache over red chalk.

The drawing agrees exactly with the painting.

ROME, S. Catarina a Magnanapoli
ST. CATHERINE RECEIVING THE TWO CROSSES FROM CHRIST

Painting over sacristy door (cf. Waterhouse, p. 85).

569. STUDY FOR THE WHOLE COMPOSITION   (0272)

215 × 170 mm. Oval. Pen and brown wash, heightened with white, over red chalk.

ROME, S. Francesco a Ripa
THE FLIGHT INTO EGYPT

Painting in the third chapel on the right. Probably executed after 1708 (cf. Waterhouse, p. 85).

570. DRAWING FOR THE WHOLE COMPOSITION   (0274)

228 × 171 mm. Pen and brown wash, with white and grey gouache over red chalk.

THE PIETA

Painting at present hung over the main entrance to the church.

571. STUDY FOR THE WHOLE DESIGN   (0278)

234 × 180 mm. Pen and brown wash, heightened with white, over red chalk.

The painting differs in many details from the drawing, which is, however, probably a preliminary sketch for it. Another drawing of the same theme, similar in character, is in the Albertina.

ROME, S. Maria in Araceli
THE ASSUMPTION OF THE VIRGIN

Painting on wall of nave (cf. Waterhouse, p. 85).

572. STUDY FOR THE WHOLE COMPOSITION   (0263)

248 × 271 mm. Pen and brown wash, heightened with white and grey gouache over red chalk. Squared.

2. *Drawings connected with an engraved composition*

THE DEPOSITION

Composition engraved by Westerhout and used in Alessandro Mazzinelli's *Uffizio della Settimana Santa*, Rome, 1744.

573. STUDY FOR THE WHOLE COMPOSITION   (0276)

157 × 109 mm. Pen and brown wash, heightened with white and grey gouache.

574. THE DESCENT FROM THE CROSS   (0277)

132 × 90 mm. Pen and brown wash, heightened with white and grey gouache.

Perhaps an alternative design for No.573.

3. *Drawings not connected with known works*

575. THE SACRIFICE OF MANOAH   (0261)

236 × 182 mm. Pen and brown wash, heightened with white and grey gouache, over red chalk.

The usual renderings of this subject show the angel disappearing in the flame from the sacrifice, but in this version Passeri has followed a rarer pattern, with the angel setting light to the sacrifice, which is found, for instance, in a painting by Tintoretto at Gothenburg (cf. Bercken, *Tintoretto*, Munich, 1942, Pl. 8).

576. THE FLIGHT INTO EGYPT   (0269)

228 × 183 mm. Pen and brown wash, heightened with white over red chalk.

577. THE LAST SUPPER   (0265)

75 × 160 mm. Pen and brown wash, heightened with white.

578. THE FLAGELLATION   (0275)

148 × 144 mm. Pen and brown wash, heightened with white and grey gouache, on brown paper.

579. THE VIRGIN AND CHILD ADORED BY A BISHOP AND A MONK   (0262)

382 × 238 mm. Pen and brown wash, heightened with white and grey gouache over red chalk. Squared.

580. THE VIRGIN ADORED BY ST. FRANCIS AND TAKING THE CHRIST CHILD FROM ST. CHRISTOPHER   (0271)

Circular, c.220 mm. in diameter. Pen and brown wash, heightened with white and grey gouache over red chalk.

The theme of the Virgin taking Christ from St. Christopher seems to be very rare.

581. THE DECAPITATION OF TWO MARTYRS   (0268)

261 × 178 mm. Pen and brown wash, heightened with white over red chalk.

The martyrs might be Sts. Cosmas and Damian, but the presence of other victims in the background being beaten, apparently on their way to execution is an argument against this identification.

582. THE TRIUMPH OF ST. THOMAS AQUINAS (*Plate 62*)   (5204)

307 × 450 mm. Pen and brown wash, heightened with white over red chalk.

A youthful figure, with a sun on his monk's habit, sits in a chariot drawn by two horses. He points to a book held out by a bearded man, beside whom are two putti carrying a crucifix. Two angels fly behind carrying books, and another flies ahead blowing a trumpet. The chariot wheels crush a prostrate figure, and another (?Heresy) shrinks away in the left foreground. In the centre a man presents to the hero of the scene a book supported by two boys, and on the right a woman draws the attention of a man to the scene.

583. A HERO CROWNED BY VICTORY   (0264)

224 × 216 mm. Pen and brown wash, heightened with white over red chalk. A narrow strip of paper added at the top.

A hero in armour stands in the centre of the composition, while a figure of Victory holds a crown over his head. Before him kneels a bound captive, behind whom is a lion. A second lion is on the right, and beside it are two putti, one carrying an olive branch. In the foreground is a cornucopia.

584. ERMINIA AND THE SHEPHERDS   (0273)

127 × 190 mm. Pen and brown wash, heightened with white over red chalk.

585. A BATTLE OUTSIDE A WALLED TOWN (*Plate 63*)   (0266)

227 × 336 mm. Pen and brown wash, heightened with white and grey gouache, over red chalk.

586. AN ARMY MARCHING OUT OF A WALLED TOWN   (0267)

206 × 313 mm. Pen and brown wash, heightened with white and grey wash, on a red-tinted background.

Two scenes, apparently from the same series, to which a drawing in Düsseldorf (No.402) must also belong. The latter is called 'Semiramis marching to save Babylon', but the reason for this title is not clear. The Gothic gateway in No. 586 suggests rather that the subject is mediaeval, perhaps connected with the crusades, and the capture of Jerusalem. If so, the drawings no doubt form part of a series illustrating Tasso. A drawing by Passeri illustrating a scene from the *Gerusalemme* is at Holkham.

587. SOLDIERS CARRYING OFF A WOMAN   (6806)

167 × 233 mm. Pen and brown wash, heightened with white over red chalk.

On the right three soldiers, one on horseback, carry off a woman who appeals for help to her companions.

The drawing is without traditional attribution, but the style is certainly Passeri's.

PIETRO BERETTINI
(called PIETRO DA CORTONA)
(1596–1669)

The greater part of the drawings here catalogued as by, or connected with, Pietro da Cortona come from three volumes made up in the eighteenth century and listed in Inventory A. Two of these, which consisted of numbers 4441–4480 and 4508–4547, contained only drawings ascribed to Cortona, whereas the third (Nos. 4481–4507) was described as being devoted to Cortona, Ferri, Romanelli, Salvator Rosa, and others. It might be expected from this that the drawings in the first two volumes would sustain critical examination as works of Cortona better than those in the third, but this is not actually the case, and more than half of their contents have been relegated to other sections of the catalogue. More than twenty have been classified as from the hand or the studio of Giovanni Paolo Schor, while others have either been left among the anonymous drawings, or have been put with those attributed to the various members of Cortona's studio who can be recognised with some degree of certainty.

It must, however, be emphasised that in the present state of our knowledge the distinction between Cortona's own drawings and those of his studio is extremely uncertain. Ciro Ferri in his black chalk drawings,

Fig. 57   P. da Cortona, Prado Museum

Romanelli in his pen and wash sketches, Schor in his decorative designs, all come so close to the manner of their master that a firm borderline cannot be drawn. On the other hand the Royal Collection supplies some twenty-five drawings which can be related to known works of Cortona, though not all of these are certainly original, and some are evidently copies or by studio hands. But this group gives a basis for further attributions, and a number of drawings emerge which are of such good quality and so close to the manner of the assured drawings that they can properly be attributed to Cortona himself. Unfortunately only one of the certain drawings (No.588 for Castelfusano) is early (c.1627–29), but evidence about Cortona's manner a few years later is supplied by a drawing in the Prado (Fig.57), which, though not there attributed to him, is certainly original, since it was engraved in Ferrari's *Flora*, which appeared in 1633. The very personal use of hatching in body-colour is to be found in exactly the same form in the drawing of *Samson killing the Philistine* (No.611), in which the types are also Cortonesque. Precisely the same technique appears in two other drawings which at first sight do not look like Cortona's work: the *Fall of the Damned* (No.609) and the *Sacrifice of Isaac* (No.610). In both drawings the poses and the crowded

compositions show traces of Mannerism unusual in Cortona, but certain heads are like his later types, and the drawings show that unkempt and matted hair which was to become a regular characteritsic of his drawings and paintings. How Mannerist his early drawings can be is proved by a study in Rennes for one of the S. Bibiana frescoes of 1624–26. I would suggest that the two drawings at Windsor might well be between 1625 and 1630, when Cortona had evolved a new technique but had not fully thrown off the effects of his early training.

In his maturity Cortona continued to use body-colour for modelling, but he generally applies it in broader touches, though even in a drawing like the *Conversion of St. Paul* (No.614) traces of the early manner can be seen. At the same time his black chalk technique becomes freer, as for instance in the design for the Pace (No.594), which presumably dates from about 1656–57. The extraordinary vigour of his late drawings can be seen in the sketch for the ceiling of the Palazzo Pamphili (No.605).

Cortona's power as an architectural draughtsman is admirably displayed in the drawing for his tomb (No. 592) and the large design for the Quarantore in S. Lorenzo in Damaso (No.591).

The question of Cortona's copies after ancient sculpture is one that needs further study, but a few of the vast mass of drawings in the Pozzo collection seem to come so close to his manner that they deserve to be listed in this context.

1. Drawings connected with known works

CASTEL FUSANO, Villa Sacchetti
The ceiling in the Gallery was executed by Cortona and assistants in 1627–29 (cf. Waterhouse, p. 57).

588. THE TRIUMPH OF BACCHUS   (4515)
326 × 210 mm. Pen and brown ink, brown wash, heightened with white.

Lit.: K. T. Parker, *Catalogue of the collection of Drawings in the Ashmolean Museum*, ii, 1956, p. 439.

Study for the composition at one end of the ceiling.

FLORENCE, Palazzo Pitti
The state rooms on the piano nobile were decorated by Cortona between 1641 and 1647 (cf. H. Geisenheimer, *Pietro da Cortona e gli affreschi nel Palazzo Pitti*, Florence, 1909, and Voss, p. 539).

589. STUDY FOR CEILING DECORATION   (4446)
332 × 449 mm. Pen and brown ink, brown and grey washes, over black chalk.

This drawing does not correspond exactly to any of the executed decoration, but in general disposition it is close to several, perhaps most particularly to the Sala di Venere.

Fig. 58   Cat. No. 591

PARIS, Louvre
MADONNA AND CHILD WITH S. MARTINA

The painting, a late work, executed for Louis XIV, is reproduced in Voss, p. 260.

590. HEAD OF THE MADONNA (4531)

236 × 175 mm. Black chalk, brown wash, touches of white, on dark-brown paper.

ROME, S. Lorenzo in Damaso

Decorations for the Quarantore, executed in February 1633. The decorations are exactly described in a document quoted by Pollak (*Die Kunsttätigkeit unter Urban VIII*, Vienna, 1928–31, i, p. 163).

591. DRAWING FOR THE WHOLE SCHEME (*Fig. 58*) (4448)

398 × 568 mm. Pen and brown wash over black chalk.

The drawing shows the whole interior, but only part of it is finished, the rest being only indicated in outline.

The identification of the subject of this drawing is due to Dr. K. Noehles, who has kindly allowed his discovery to be published in this catalogue.

ROME, SS. Luca e Martina

592. DESIGN FOR THE ARTIST'S TOMB (*Fig. 59*) (4449)

345 × 169 mm. Fine pen, brown wash, over black chalk indications.

The head conforms closely to that shown in the Uffizi *Self-Portrait* of 1664 (cf. *Catalogue of the Mostra di Pietro da Cortona*, Cortona, 1956, No.44, Pl. xlviii), but shows a much younger man. The general design of the tomb recalls Cortona's early monuments, such as the Montauti tomb in S. Gerolamo della Carità (1629), and the Landri tombs in S. Lorenzo fuori le Mura (c.1630). It is, therefore, plausible to suppose that it may be the design for the tomb which the artist proposed to erect for himself in the chapel of S. Martina under the church of S. Luca. Permission was given to him in 1634 to use this chapel, but the scheme was abandoned owing to the discovery of the body of S. Martina, which led to the chapel being enlarged and consecrated entirely to her devotion. As a consequence the artist abandoned his project for the tomb (cf. O. Pollak, *Kunsttätigkeit unter Urban VIII*, Vienna, 1928–31, i, pp. 185 ff.).

ROME, S. Maria della Pace

The church was restored and the façade added by Cortona

Fig. 59   Cat. No. 592

in 1656–57 at the order of Alexander VII (cf. Wittkower, *Art and Architecture in Italy 1600–1750*, London, 1958, p. 159).

593. STUDY FOR THE ARCH BETWEEN NAVE AND CROSSING   (4451)

235 × 380 mm. Pen and brown wash over black chalk.

The arch is visible in the engraving in Falda's *Il Nuovo teatro delle fabriche . . . di Roma moderna*, 1665, i, Pl. 27. In the executed version the allegorical figures, which, according to Titi, are by Fancelli, have been slightly altered in pose and given clear attributes of Truth and Religion. The arms are those of Pope Julius II, who allowed the Chigi family to quarter those of della Rovere.

594. STUDY FOR FRESCO IN A SPANDREL OVER ONE OF THE CHAPELS OF THE NAVE (*Fig. 60*)   (4509)

255 × 323 mm. Black chalk.

The drawing shows Moses with two other Prophets, a group which corresponds iconographically to the fresco by Raphael in the upper stage of the wall over the Chigi Chapel (reproduced in Fischel, *Raphael*, London, 1948, Pl. 196). On the other hand, the shape of the drawing corresponds to the lower stage of the frescoed zone. Mr. Vitzthum has pointed out that the shield indicated in this drawing corresponds to that over the first chapel on the left, and Cortona's fresco was, therefore, no doubt planned for this position, opposite Raphael's *Sibyls*.

What appears to be the design for the other side of the arch is in the Albertina, formerly ascribed to Cortona, but now to Ferri (*Die Zeichnungen der Toskanischen, Umbrischen und Römischen Schulen*, No.747).

ROME, St. Peter's, Chapel of the SS. Sacramento
THE HOLY TRINITY

Painted in 1628 (cf. Pollak, *Die Kunsttätigkeit unter Urban VIII*, ii, p. 272. Engraved in E. Pistolesi, *Il Vaticano*, 1829, i. Pl. 20.

595. STUDY FOR THE GROUP OF ANGELS   (4533)

205 × 307 mm. Pen and brown ink, blue washes.

Study for the lower half of the painting. At Holkham is a very free drawing, which appears to be for the figure of Christ.

ROME, Palazzo Barberini
SALONE

596. ALLEGORY OF PIETY AND CHASTITY   (6832)

262 × 598 mm. Pen, grey and brown washes over black chalk, heightened with white, on several pieces of paper of irregular shape superimposed or joined together.

Lit.: A. Blunt, *Journal of the Warburg and Courtauld Institutes*, xxi, 1958, p. 283 note 68.

A copy, apparently by the same hand as Nos.243 and 244, and therefore probably by Filippo Lauri. Two copies of other parts of the ceiling, apparently by the same hand, are in the Ashmolean (Nos.829, 830), and another is in the Louvre (No.560).

597. VENUS AND CUPIDS   (4495)

236 × 384 mm. Black chalk, heightened with white, on grey paper.

A copy after the left-hand group in the same composition.

598. THREE STUDIES OF LIONS   (4434)

186 × 255 mm. Red chalk.

Inv. A, p. 110: 'Pietro de Petris, Masucci and other Scholars of Carlo Maratti . . .'.

The top left-hand study was used almost exactly in the decoration at one corner of the ceiling.

Fig. 60   Cat. No. 594

CHAPEL

599. STUDY FOR THE DOME   (4456)

187 × 397 mm. Semi-circular. Pen and brown ink, brown wash, over red chalk.

Lit.: A. Blunt, *Burlington Magazine*, xcviii, 1956, p. 416 (repr. p. 414, Fig. 31); A. Blunt, *Journal of the Warburg and Courtauld Institutes*, xxi, 1958, p. 284, and Pl. 30c.

GALLERY

600. THE STORY OF CAECULUS, FOUNDER OF PRAENESTE   (6802)

298 × 360 mm. Pen, brown washes over black chalk indications, heightened with white, on blue paper. Inscribed on mount: *BORGOGNONE*.

Lit.: A. Blunt, *Journal of the Warburg and Courtauld Institutes*, xxi, 1958, p. 286, and Pl. 32c.

In spite of the old attribution to Borgognone the drawing is clearly an original by Cortona for the fresco in a gallery in the north-east part of the palace.

601. DESIGN FOR CEILING   (4452)

310 × 197 mm. Pen, brown wash, over black chalk.

Lit.: A. Blunt, *Journal of the Warburg and Courtauld Institutes*, xxi, 1958, p. 286, and Pl. 31d.

Design for part of the ceiling in the same gallery. In the ceiling itself the arms have been changed to those of the Pallavicini family.

ROME, formerly Prince Enrico Barberini Collection

602. TAPESTRY PORTIERE WITH THE ARMS OF DON TADDEO BARBERINI, PRINCIPE DI PALESTRINA (4481)

341 × 273 mm. Black chalk, heightened with white.

Inv. A, p. 113: 'Cortona, Ciro Ferri, etc.'.

Lit.: A. Blunt, *Journal of the Warburg and Courtauld Institutes*, xxi, 1958, p. 286, and Pl. 32d.

Finished study for the tapestry woven in 1632 (cf. *Bollettino d'Arte*, xxxv, 1950, p. 145, repr. p. 51).

ROME, Briganti Collection
TANCRED WOUNDED

Executed c.1625–30 (cf. *Catalogue of the Cortona Exhibition*, 1956, No.8, Pl. viii).

603. STUDY FOR THE WHOLE COMPOSITION (*Plate 19*)
                                                          (4504)

252 × 372 mm. Pen and brown wash, heightened with white and grey gouache, on brown-washed paper.

The drawing differs in many ways from the painting, but certain figures recur almost identically: the man leaning over the wounded Tancred, and the two soldiers on the extreme left.

ROME, Galleria Nazionale
THE GUARDIAN ANGEL

The painting (*Catalogue of the Cortona Exhibition*, 1956, No.42, Pl. xlvi) was commissioned by Alexander VII and paid for in July 1656.

604. STUDY FOR THE WHOLE COMPOSITION   (4519)
265 × 186 mm. Black chalk.

ROME, Palazzo Pamphili, Gallery
The Gallery was decorated by Cortona with scenes from the life of Aeneas in 1651–4 (cf. Waterhouse, p. 59).

605. THE DEATH OF TURNUS (*Plate 21*)   (4524)
166 × 236 mm. Pen and brown wash.

Study for one of the principal subjects on the ceiling. This section is reproduced in *Bollettino d'Arte*, xlii, 1957, p. 36, Fig. 10.

606. JUNO APPEALING TO AEOLUS TO SET FREE THE WINDS   (4526)
164 × 141 mm. Pen and brown ink, brown wash, over black chalk.

Study for one of the oval panels on the ceiling. In the fresco itself (repr. *ibid.*, p. 32, Fig. 6) the composition is reversed and the peacocks are pushed into the background.

2. Drawings connected with works known from engravings

TULLIA DRIVING HER CHARIOT OVER THE BODY OF HER FATHER

Engraved by Lempereur after Cortona.

607. DRAWING FOR THE WHOLE COMPOSITION   (4514)
276 × 361 mm. Pen and brown wash, heightened with white, on brown-washed paper.

The drawing differs from the engraved design in that the body of the dead king is further to the right and the onlookers on the left are omitted. Another drawing, corresponding more closely to the engraving, but in reverse, is in the Louvre (No.492), and a third is in the Uffizi. The design was used by Giuseppe Chiari as the basis for a painting of the subject, now at Burghley.

Fig. 61   Cat. No. 609   Fig. 62   Cat. No. 610

ALEXANDER ASSAULTING PERA
Engraved by C. Bloemaert.

608. STUDY FOR THE WHOLE COMPOSITION (*Plate 17*)
                                                              (01121)

488 × 719 mm. Pen and brown wash, retouched with grey gouache. Inv. A, p. 158, as Cortona.

A red chalk drawing of the figure of Alexander in the Louvre (No.498), in reverse, is certainly a copy. A fine partial study is at Düsseldorf (No.358); one in the Farnesina (No.128790) is related to the design, but is probably not by Cortona. A large drawing at Holkham, similar in style but entirely different in composition, probably represents the same subject.

3. Drawings not connected with known works

609. THE FALL OF THE DAMNED (*Fig. 61*)   (4508)

331 × 460 mm. Pen and brown wash, heightened with white, on white paper, much darkened.

Presumably from the bottom of a composition of the Last Judgment. Close in style to No.610, and probably dating from about the same period.

610. THE SACRIFICE OF ISAAC (*Fig. 62*)   (4485)

288 × 192 mm. Blue and grey washes, heightened with white, over black chalk, on grey paper.

The drawing is in many ways unusual for Cortona. The design is full of Mannerist elements, such as the crowding of the space and the pose of Isaac, but the heads of Abraham and the angel are Cortonesque, and the technique is typical of his early work. The drawing probably dates from a very early period, when the artist was still under the influence of Commodi.

611. SAMSON KILLING THE PHILISTINE (*Plate 22*)(4540)

218 × 163 mm. Pen and brown ink, modelled with white and blue gouache, on blue-grey paper.

The style is that of Cortona in his early phase, c.1630–35 (cf. Fig. 57).

612. THE MASSACRE OF THE INNOCENTS   (6834)

341 × 492 mm. Pen and brown wash, heightened with white over black chalk, on white paper much darkened.

In the foreground three groups: on the left a kneeling mother protecting her child from a soldier; in the centre a soldier pursues a mother holding her child; on the right a soldier tramples on a child and thrusts aside the mother. In the background similar scenes take place on the steps of a temple. The technique and style suggest that the drawing dates from the 1630s.

613. NOLI ME TANGERE   (4484)

282 × 240 mm. Pen and brown ink, with white and blue gouache, on grey paper. Inscribed in the 'deceptive' hand: *Cortona*.

The Magdalene kneels on the left beside a basket before Christ, who stands on the right holding a long-handled spade. Two paintings of the subject by Cortona are known, one in the Hermitage, the other formerly in the Hamilton Palace collection (sale, 1882, lot No.707). Both are similar to the drawing in general conception, but not so close that the latter can be considered an actual preparatory study. A third painting connected with the design was exhibited as by Giuseppe Chiari at Colnaghi's in 1958.

614. THE CONVERSION OF ST. PAUL (*Plate 18*)   (4510)

308 × 465 mm. Pen and brown wash, heightened with white, blue and grey gouache.

The figure of St. Paul recurs in almost identical form in an altarpiece in S. Giovanni Battista, Velletri, formerly ascribed to Cortona, but now considered to be by Lazzaro Baldi (cf. Catalogue of the Cortona exhibition, Palazzo Barberini, Rome, 1956, p. 20).

615. THE MARTYRDOM OF ST. PAUL   (4503)

220 × 361 mm. Pen and brown wash, heightened with white and blue gouache, over black chalk, on grey-brown paper. St. Paul, beheaded, lies in the centre, while a fountain springs up beside his decapitated head. On the left the executioner sheathes his sword; on the right soldiers and other figures look on in astonishment. In the background other soldiers and the walls of Rome.

616. A SAINT RECEIVING A PAIR OF MANACLES FROM THE VIRGIN (*Plate 23*)   (4483)

312 × 217 mm. Black chalk and brown wash.

A mature drawing of the middle period. The same subject is known in an engraving by G. Castel after Ciro Ferri.

617. DESIGN FOR PART OF THE FRAME FOR AN ALTARPIECE   (4472)

187 × 123 mm. Pen and brown wash over black chalk, on brown-washed paper.

The drawing shows the figure of an angel supporting the side of a curved frame.

618. STUDY OF A MALE NUDE, SEATED ON THE GROUND, LEFT LEG EXTENDED   (4528)

247 × 325 mm. Red chalk.

619. A MALE NUDE, STANDING, IN FRONT OF A TREE

354 × 252 mm. Red chalk. Unfinished.   (4529)

620. A MALE NUDE, POISED IN THE ACT OF RUNNING, WEARING A CLOAK   (4530)

375 × 253 mm. Red chalk.

621. STUDY OF A SEATED MALE NUDE   (5538)

559 × 423 mm. Red chalk on buff paper. Inscribed: *Cave Bernini*.

In spite of the old inscription this is a characteristic drawing by Cortona.

PIETRO DA CORTONA
(attributed to)

622. AUGUSTUS AND THE SIBYL (*Plate 20*)   (4517)

270 × 388 mm. Black chalk.

Lit.: C. H. Collins Baker, *Catalogue of the Pictures at Hampton Court*, London, 1929, p. 116; S. von Below, *Beiträge zur Kenntnis Pietro da Cortonas*, Murnau, 1932, p. 44.

Connected with a painting executed for La Vrillière and now at Nancy. Other versions are at Hampton Court Palace and in the Ringling Museum, Sarasota.
Mr. Walter Vitzthum and Dr. Briganti both consider this drawing to be a variant by Ferri based on Cortona's painting rather than a study for it by Cortona himself. Mr. Vitzthum has called attention to an original study for the painting in the Graphische Sammlung, Munich (No.6792). Another drawing connected with the composition is in the Albertina (*Zeichnungen der Toskanischen, Umbrischen und Römischen Schulen*, No.725).

623. STUDY OF A MALE NUDE, SEATED, LEFT LEG RAISED AND ARMS EXTENDED   (4437)

554 × 405 mm. Red chalk, heightened with white. Inscribed in black chalk: *Pietro da Cortona*.

624. STUDY OF A MALE NUDE STANDING ON A ROCK   (4438)

549 × 405 mm. Red chalk. Inscribed in ink (partly erased): *Pietro Beretino*, and in black chalk: *Pietro da Cortona*.

625. STUDY OF A MALE NUDE, SEEN FROM BEHIND, LEANING UPON A CRUTCH   (4439)

556 × 353 mm. Red chalk, heightened with white. Inscribed in black chalk: *Pietro da Cortona*.

626. STUDY OF A MALE NUDE, SEATED, SEEN FROM BEHIND, FACING TO LEFT   (4440)

516 × 400 mm. Red chalk, heightened with white. Inscribed in black chalk: *Pietro da Cortona*.

In spite of their old inscriptions these academies are feeble in comparison with similar works from Cortona's own hand, and they are probably by a member of his studio.

627. FRAGMENT OF AN ANCIENT ENTABLATURE   (4459)

157 × 140 mm. Pen and bistre wash.

628. THE BASE OF AN ANCIENT COLUMN   (10748)

184 × 236 mm. Pen and brown ink over black chalk.

629. DRAWING AFTER A SARCOPHAGUS WITH THE DEATH OF MELEAGER   (8718)

172 × 573 mm. Pen and brown ink, with grey wash.
Verso: A wreath of oak leaves.
The sarcophagus is in the Villa Pamphili.

630. DRAWING AFTER A SARCOPHAGUS WITH THE TRIUMPH OF BACCHUS   (8648)

137 × 378 mm. Pen and brown ink, with grey wash.
The sarcophagus is in the Villa Pamphili.

631. DRAWING AFTER THE BASE OF A COLUMN   (8373)

238 × 263 mm. Pen and brown ink, with grey wash. Numbered: *32*.
The base is in the Villa Pamphili.

632. DRAWING OF A SEATED DEITY   (8805)

235 × 163 mm. Pen and black ink, with black wash over black chalk.

The statue, of which only the lower half survives, is at Naples.

633. DRAWING OF AN IMPERIAL STANDARD   (11152)

740 × 250 mm. Pen and brown ink, with grey wash. Numbered: *606*.

These drawings after the Antique all come from the collection of Cassiano dal Pozzo. Many others in his volumes seem to be by members of Cortona's studio (cf. above, p. 76).

Fig. 63

PIETRO DA CORTONA
(studio of)

RECONSTRUCTION OF THE TEMPLE OF PRAENESTE

634. 625×940 mm. Pen and black ink, with light brown
wash.   (10382)

635. 1015×625 mm. Pen and brown wash.   (10383)

636. 420×1093 mm. Pen and brown wash.   (10384)

Lit.: Ashby, in *Papers of the British School at Rome*, ix, 1920,
No.245; R. Wittkower, in *Adolph Goldschmidt zu seinem
siebenzigsten Geburtstag*, 1933, Nos.137–43.

Exh.: 17th Century Art, Royal Academy, London, 1938, No.
634.

Studio drawings, showing plan, perspective view, and elevation of Cortona's proposed reconstruction of the temple,
made for the Barberini, who had bought Palestrina from the
Colonna family. The original of No.636 is in the Victoria
and Albert Museum.

Cat. No. 637

637. THE VICTORY OF ALEXANDER OVER PORUS
   (Fig. 63)   (12064)

852 × 1580 mm. Pen and brown wash, on six pieces of paper.

A confused battle with Alexander in the centre, charging on a horse, and Porus on the right, fleeing on his elephant.

This unusually large and finished drawing was presumably made as a preparation for a big battle-piece similar to *The Victory of Alexander over Darius*, which Cortona executed for the Sacchetti c.1635 (cf. Cortona Exhibition, 1956, No.27), and may even have been planned as a pair to it.

The composition is entirely Cortona's, but the execution lacks vigour, and the details of handling suggest that it was probably carried out by Giacomo Cortese, who worked in his studio and was a specialist in the painting and drawing of horses.

The composition is in many ways related to Cortese's battle-scenes in the Collegio Romano and the Quirinal (cf. F. A. Salvagnini, *I Pittori Borgognoni Cortese*, Rome, 1937, Pls. xliv, xlvi, xlvii and liii).

638. DESIGN FOR A TOMB (4450)

370 × 171 mm. Pen and grey wash, on brown paper, over black chalk. Inscribed: *Pietro di Cortona Annag. Corona de' Pittori*.

In spite of the inscription the bust bears no likeness to the artist, and the arms at the top are those of the Barberini, with a cardinal's hat. The forms of the tomb are Cortonesque, but the execution is that of a not very competent pupil.

639 DESIGN FOR A CEILING (4447)

354 × 592 mm. Pen over black chalk. On four pieces of paper, joined irregularly.

Part of a ceiling with circular, semi-circular, square, etc., panels surrounded with heavily ornamented framework and decorated with swags and volutes, supported by putti and other figures.

640. DESIGN FOR A FRIEZE (10911)

156 × 364 mm. Pen and brown wash.

The allegorical figure of Justice accompanied by putti. The architectural details are typical of Cortona, but the drawing, with its minute touches with the point of the brush, is unusually precise for him. A design for a looking-glass in the Metropolitan Museum (No.49.19.72), inscribed with the name of Cortona, is by the same hand, and a very similar drawing, ascribed to Romanelli, is in the Witt collection, Courtauld Institute of Art (No.4188). Another, for a lectern, in the British Museum (Cracherode, Ff.3.194), is attributed to Ciro Ferri, who may in fact be the author of the whole group.

PIETRO DA CORTONA
(follower of)
SCENES FROM THE LIFE OF A DOMINICAN OR CARMELITE NUN

Nine small drawings, probably intended to be engraved for a life of the nun, whose identity has not so far been established. In view of the coat of arms on No.645, she may have been a member of the Torrigiani or Torresani families.

641. THE NUN RECEIVING A HABIT FROM A PRIEST (6770a)

90 × 67 mm. Pen and brown wash, heightened with white and grey gouache.

642. CHRIST APPEARS TO THE NUN AS SHE SITS WRITING IN HER CELL (6770b)

90 × 67 mm. Pen and brown wash, heightened with white and grey gouache.

643. CHRIST, HOLDING A THUNDERBOLT, APPEARS TO THE NUN (6771)

98 × 76 mm. Pen and brown wash, heightened with white and grey gouache. An illegible inscription at the bottom, which might be an *Imprimatur*.
Christ points to buildings like Roman Thermae, as if threatening their destruction.

644. KING DAVID APPEARS TO THE NUN (6772)

104 × 69 mm. Black and white chalk, with brown wash, on grey-blue paper.

645. THE CHRIST CHILD APPEARS TO THE NUN AS SHE KNEELS BEFORE AN ALTAR (6769a)

89 × 70 mm. Pen and brown wash, heightened with grey and white gouache.

Beside the altar is a shield, to which the nun points, and which bears as a coat of arms a tower surmounted by three stars. These appear to be the arms of the Torrigiani or the Torresani family.

646. THE NUN AND HER COMPANIONS ARE GUIDED THROUGH A WOOD AT NIGHT BY ANGELS WITH TORCHES (6769b)

89 × 70 mm. Pen and brown wash, heightened with grey and white gouache.

647. THE NUN SITS IN A GARDEN PRAYING FOR SOULS IN PURGATORY (6773)

103 × 89 mm. Pen and brown wash, heightened with white.

648. THE NUN KNEELS BEFORE AN ALTAR IN A CROWDED CHURCH (6774a)

80 × 63 mm. Silver point.

649. CHRIST APPEARS TO THE NUN ON HER DEATH-BED (6774b)

80 × 63 mm. Silver point.

In Inventory A (p. 128) these drawings are attributed to 'a good scholar of P. da Cortona'. The closest parallel seems to be a drawing at Holkham of *Christ appearing to a nun*, ascribed to Ciro Ferri.

650. ALLEGORY OF RELIGION (6807)

259 × 159 mm. Pen and brown wash, heightened with white and grey gouache, on brown paper.

Inv. A, p. 128: From a volume containing Guglielmo Borgognone, Baciccia, Baldi, etc.

At the bottom sits Justice holding the scales and leaning on a book; above to the right Religion, with a cross; and above again, but to the left, a female figure holding the Papal Tiara, over which hovers the Dove in a radiance.
Similar in technique to the last group, and probably by the same hand.

651. THE CRUCIFIXION (4493)

284 × 187 mm. Pen and brown wash, heightened with white.
St. John and the two Marys at the foot of the Cross.

This is a variation of a composition by Cortona known in two drawings (at Holkham and in the British Museum), the former being connected with the Altarpiece at Castel Gandolfo.

652. STUDY FOR A CRUCIFIED CHRIST (5535)

528 × 358 mm. Red chalk on buff paper. Inscribed: *Cav.ᵉ Bernini*.

A drawing in the manner of Cortona, but too weak for him.

653. STUDIES OF A LION (4478)

226 × 333 mm. Two lions in red, and two in black chalk.

Verso: Three studies of lions and one of a goat. Red chalk, with touches of black.

Inv. A, p. 112, as Cortona.

Similar in style to No.598, which is a preliminary study for the Barberini ceiling.

654. THE ADORATION OF THE SHEPHERDS (4499)

217 × 331 mm. The design is oval, the paper oblong. Black and white chalk and brown wash, on blue-grey paper.

Inscribed in the 'deceptive' hand: *Cortona*.

655. THE TEMPTATION OF ST. ANTHONY (6839)

323 × 568 mm. Pen and brown wash, heightened with white, on grey-blue paper.

656. A GROUP OF WOMEN ON THE STEPS OF AN ALTAR, ADORING THE BLESSED SACRAMENT (4488)

415 × 270 mm. Pen and brown ink, brown washes, heightened with white, over preliminary black chalk.

Inv. A, p. 113: 'P. Cortona, Ciro Ferri, Romanelli, Salvator Rosa, &c.'.

657. AN ALTAR, SUPPORTING A CHALICE AND SURROUNDED BY ANGELS (4482)

352 × 260 mm. Black chalk.

On the altar is an oval medallion with a pelican feeding her young.

658. AN ANGEL CARRYING AN OVAL MEDALLION OF THE VIRGIN AND CHILD (4474)

154 × 122 mm. Pen and brown ink, with black wash.

659. AN ANGEL (4473)

161 × 131 mm. Black wash over black chalk.

Berninesque in type, but Cortonesque in technique.

660. THE SACRIFICE OF IPHIGENIA (3748)

466 × 396 mm. Black and white chalk.

661. VENUS AND CUPID APPEARING BEFORE JUPITER (6820)

216 × 453 mm. The drawing itself is oval. Black chalk, with grey and some brown wash.

A variant of Cortona's version of the same subject in the ceiling of the Palazzo Pamphili.

662. ROMULUS AND REMUS (5312)

291 × 197 mm. Pen and brown wash over black chalk.

Verso: Two men looking down, and a group of men pulling a winch. Black chalk.

663. THE RAPE OF THE SABINES (4479)

273 × 496 mm. Fan-shaped. Pen and brown ink, with black wash.

Perhaps a design for a fan.

664. THE JUSTICE OF TRAJAN (6831)

339 × 571 mm. Grey washes, touches of white chalk, over black chalk outlines and shading, on blue paper.

665. A KING SACRIFICING (6816)

207 × 281 mm. Pen and brown ink, with grey wash and body-colour.

A feeble drawing by an artist trained in Cortona's early style.

666. DESIGN FOR A CEILING (4453)

233 × 331 mm. Pen and brown ink over black chalk.

The corner section of a ceiling, with a Cortonesque frame surrounding the central field. The cove is decorated illusionistically with a balustrade on which lean figures. The general disposition of the design recalls the frescoes of Andrea Pozzo in the Convento del S. Cuore at the Trinità dei Monti, Rome (cf. *Commentari*, x, 1959, Pls. xi and xii).

PIETRO DE PIETRI
(1663–1716)

Inventory A, p. 110, records: '10 heads in red and black chalk with drawings on the back of two by Pietro de Petris.' These can be identified as Inventory Nos.4396–4405, two of which (Nos.4399 and 4405) have drawings of hands, etc. on the *verso*. (No.4397 has on the *verso* another head like those on the *rectos*.) In spite of the old attribution of this series to Pietro de Pietri, two drawings (Nos.4303, 4304) must be rejected as being in a quite different style, much more closely allied to that of Masucci.

A further group is defined on p. 110 as follows: '21 Ditto of Pietro de Petris and five of the school of Carlo Maratti.' These correspond to Nos.5644–5664, which include a complete study for the painting in S. Maria in Via Lata (No.5649); but again certain drawings (Nos.5644–7, 5650, 5651, 5654) must be rejected on style.

A third group is described on p. 110 as '33 Drawings of Pietro de Petris, Massucci and other Scholars of Carlo Maratti'. These correspond to Nos.4406 to 4436, the difference in number being due to the fact that in two cases there are two drawings on one mount. Here the attribution of any particular drawing is clearly left more open, but two of the group (Nos.4409a and b) are studies for paintings by Pietro de Pietri in S. Maria via Lata, and two others (Nos.4412, 4413) are preparations for a painting by him in S. Clemente. The technique of the latter pair, with full water-colour, is so unusual that it makes certain the attribution to Pietro de Pietri of several others in the group (Nos.4411, 4419). One of these, of the *Assumption* (No.4419), is closely related to drawings in the second group (Nos.5660, 5663, 5664).

On the basis of this evidence it is possible to form a fairly clear idea of the drawing style of this second-rate follower of Maratta.

Fig. 64   Cat. No. 667

1. Drawings connected with known works

DIJON, Museum
THE CESSATION OF THE SCHISM OF ANACLETUS

The painting comes from the Abbey of Cîteaux and was a pendant to Passeri's *St. Bernard received into Cîteaux by St. Stephen* (cf. No.567). Hitherto it has also been ascribed to Passeri, but the drawing is certainly by Pietro de Pietri, and the painting does not appear to be by the same hand as the *St. Bernard*. The attribution to Pietro de Pietri is confirmed by the existence of another study for the composition at Holkham, traditionally and correctly ascribed to him. It is quite likely that the two commissions should have gone to two different followers of Maratta.

667. STUDY FOR THE WHOLE COMPOSITION (*Fig. 64*)
                                                 (5661)

227 × 179 mm. Pen and pale brown wash. Numbered: *135*.

ROME, S. Clemente
ST. CLEMENT GIVING THE VEIL TO S. FLAVIA DOMITILLA

Painting over the nave arcade (cf. C. Cecchelli, *San Clemente*, Rome, N.D., p. 91).

STUDIES FOR THE WHOLE COMPOSITION

668. 123 × 192 mm. Pen and brown ink, with water-colour. *Fig. 67.*   (4412)

669. 128 × 192 mm. Pen and brown ink, with water-colour.
                                                 (4413)

Lit.: K. T. Parker, *Catalogue of the collection of Drawings in the Ashmolean Museum*, ii, 1956, p. 469.
A drawing for the same composition was in the collection of Henry Harris, and one in reverse belongs to Mr. C. Loyd (exhibited, Burlington Fine Arts Club, 1925, No.47). Another drawing in the Ashmolean (No.924) may be connected with the S. Clemente series, but probably not with this particular drawing.

ROME, S. Maria in Via Lata
THE VIRGIN AND CHILD ADORED BY SAINTS

The attribution to Pietro de Pietri is based on Titi (*Descrizione*, Rome, 1763, p.319).

670. STUDY FOR THE WHOLE COMPOSITION (*Fig. 65*)
                                                 (5649)

420 × 282 mm. Black and white chalk on blue-grey paper.

THE PRESENTATION OF THE VIRGIN AND THE PRESENTATION OF CHRIST

These two ovals form the third pair of five in the two aisles and are ascribed by Titi (*loc. cit.*) to Pietro de Pietri.

Fig. 65   Cat. No. 670

Fig. 66

Fig. 66   Cat. Nos. 671–672

671. STUDY FOR THE *PRESENTATION OF CHRIST IN THE TEMPLE* (*Fig. 66*)   (4409a)

162 × 125 mm. The composition enclosed in an oval. Pen and brown wash over red chalk.

672. STUDY FOR THE *PRESENTATION OF THE VIRGIN IN THE TEMPLE* (*Fig. 66*)   (4409b)

162 × 125 mm. The composition enclosed in an oval. Pen and brown wash over red chalk.

The relation of the two drawings to the paintings is somewhat curious and can be explained on the assumption that originally the canvases were to be reversed in position, *i.e.* that the *Presentation of the Virgin* was to be in the right aisle, and the *Presentation of Christ* in the left. In each painting Pietro de Pietri has followed the drawing in the figures of the priest and the onlookers, but has interchanged the principal group so that in the *Presentation of the Virgin* the priest faces left, and in the *Presentation of Christ* he faces right. Apart from this curious juggling of the main figures the correspondences are extremely close.

2. Drawings not connected with known works

673. THE BIRTH OF THE VIRGIN   (4429)

327 × 248 mm. Black chalk.

674. THE NATIVITY   (5653)

287 × 219 mm. Black chalk.

THE ADORATION OF THE SHEPHERDS

675. 337 × 262 mm. Black chalk.   (4430)

676. 266 × 207 mm. Black chalk.   (4432)

677. THE HOLY FAMILY   (4406)

150 × 142 mm. Red chalk.

Verso: St. Joseph with the Christ Child.

THE PRESENTATION

678. 260 × 191 mm. Red chalk.   (4408)

Fig. 67   Cat. No. 668

Fig. 68   Cat. No. 697

679. 260 × 196 mm. Pen and brown wash.   (4425)

680. 322 × 198 mm. Black chalk.   (4178)
The last drawing is from the Maratta volumes.

The central group is in general terms connected with the oval painting of the same subject in S. Maria in Via Lata. Another painting of the theme was in the Palazzo Pallavicini in the eighteenth century (cf. E. Wright, *Some observations made in travelling through France, Italy . . .* , London, 1730, i, p. 295).

For a drawing for the kneeling figure in the foreground, see No.698.

680a. THE DECAPITATION OF ST. JOHN THE BAPTIST
330 × 216 mm. Black chalk.   (5652)

681. THE INSTITUTION OF THE EUCHARIST   (5662)
227 × 156 mm. Pen and brown wash, heightened with white and grey gouache.

682. THE LAMENTATION OVER THE DEAD CHRIST
251 × 203 mm. Black chalk.   (4410)

GOD THE FATHER WITH THE DEAD CHRIST
683. 302 × 199 mm. Black chalk.   (5656)

684. 303 × 198 mm. Black chalk.   (4433)

685. THE ASSUMPTION   (4419)
190 × 191 mm. Pen and brown ink, with water-colour.

THE ASSUMPTION, WITH ST. PHILIP NERI AND ST. FRANCIS
686. 187 × 136 mm. Pen and brown wash over black chalk.   (5663)
687. 258 × 177 mm. Pen and brown wash, heightened with white and grey gouache.   (5664)

687a. 401 × 272 mm. Black and white chalk on grey-green paper.   (5660)
Verso: Studies of hands and a head. Black and white chalk, one hand in red.
A drawing for the same composition is in the British Museum (No.1946–2–9–34).

688. THE VIRGIN AND CHILD ADORED BY ST. ANTHONY OF PADUA   (5655)
247 × 200 mm. Black chalk.

689. THE VIRGIN AND CHILD ADORED BY A DOMINICAN MONK   (5657)
397 × 263 mm. Black and white chalk on grey-green paper.

ST. LOUIS PRESENTED TO THE VIRGIN AND CHILD BY ST. FRANCIS
690. 207 × 168 mm. Black chalk.   (5659)

691. 212 × 167 mm. Black chalk.   (4431)
In both drawings St. Elizabeth and the infant St. John balance the Virgin and the Christ Child.

692. THE COUNTESS MATILDA BEFORE URBAN II   (4411)
172 × 148 mm. Pen and brown ink, with water-colour.
Based on Romanelli's fresco of the same subject in the Vatican.

693. ALLEGORY IN HONOUR OF CLEMENT XI   (4436)
264 × 196 mm. Pen and brown wash over black chalk.
Probably a design for an engraving. The main composition represents figures presenting a petition to a pope, who can be identified as Clement XI by the allusion to the Albani arms in the landscape, which shows hills over which appear a rainbow and a star. In the front are allegorical figures of Justice, Religion, and Charity.

694. APELLES PAINTING CAMPASPE   (5648)
322 × 163 mm. Black chalk.

695. MARS AND VENUS DISCOVERED BY VULCAN   (5658)
367 × 257 mm. Black chalk.

STUDIES OF THE HEAD OF AN OLD MAN
696. 268 × 219 mm. Black, red and white chalk on grey-green paper.   (4405)
Verso: Studies of hands and mourning figures.

697. 321×243 mm. Black, red and white chalk on grey-green paper. (*Fig. 68*)   (4398)

698. 342×257 mm. Black, red and white chalk on grey paper.   (4399)
Verso: Kneeling figure for the 'Presentation' (cf. Nos.678–80).

699. HEAD OF A WOMAN   (4401)
264×208 mm. Black, red and white chalk on grey-green paper.
Perhaps a study for the Virgin. In general type like No.689.

700. STUDY FOR THE HEAD OF A GIRL   (4400)
267×193 mm. Black, white and coloured chalk.

701. STUDY FOR THE HEAD OF A YOUNG WOMAN   (4396)
364×267 mm. Black, red and white chalk on grey paper.

702. STUDY FOR THE HEAD OF A YOUNG WOMAN   (4397)
361×261 mm. Black, red and white chalk on grey-green paper.
Verso: Head of a young man.

703. HEAD OF A CHILD   (4402)
269×213 mm. Black, red and white chalk on grey-green paper.

704. STUDY OF A MALE NUDE PULLING ON A ROPE
510×343 mm. Black and white chalk on buff paper. (5665)

705. STUDY OF A SEATED MALE NUDE   (053)
420×265 mm. Black chalk, touches of white, on grey paper.
Inv. A, p. 147, as Pietro de Pietri.
Verso: A seated male nude pointing.

PIETRO DE PIETRI
(attributed to)

706. THE VIRGIN AND CHILD ADORED BY SAINTS (6763)
328×215 mm. Black chalk.

707. A POPE RECEIVING A VICTORIOUS GENERAL (3809)
300×266 mm. Pen and brown wash. Inscribed on a band held by putti: *Motto per Vittoria*. A poem on the *verso* (laid down) is mainly undecipherable, but may refer to the subject of the *recto*.

The turbans in the foreground and the ships in the background prove that the reference must be to a naval victory over the Turks, presumably Lepanto. If this is so, the drawing is no doubt for some decorative scheme planned by the Colonna family, who used Lepanto as the theme for the decoration of the great *Salone* in their palace in the late seventeenth century.

The attribution of this drawing to Pietro de Pietri is highly tentative, and is based on the actual tricks of draughtsmanship which recur in his certain drawings; but the general character of the drawing shows many elements of Mannerism, and the drawing may be considerably earlier.

708. A SAINT RECEIVING TWO LAYMEN   (4415)
102×68 mm. Pen and brown wash, heightened with white.
The Saint stands outside a gate, perhaps of his monastery, and appears to be defying the two visitors.

709. THE SAINT DISPUTING   (4417)
98×69 mm. Pen and brown wash, heightened with white, over traces of red chalk.

710. THE SAINT WITH THREE PILGRIMS   (4414)
102×69 mm. Pen and brown wash, heightened with white, on darkened white paper.
The Saint appears to be receiving three men, one of whom carries a pilgrim's staff.

The three drawings come from a volume containing drawings by Pietro de Pietri, Masucci, and other followers of Maratta. Allowing for the difference in scale, they come near to the pen style of Pietro de Pietri, and the types recall those in the painting of the *Cessation of the Schism of Anacletus* at Dijon (cf. above, No.667), and in another painting in the same museum, also from Cîteaux, which represents *St. Francis of Paul* and is probably also by Pietro di Pietri.

BARTOLOMEO PINELLI
(1781–1835)

711. THE SABINE WOMEN INTERVENING BETWEEN THE ROMANS AND THE SABINES   (01197)
469×636 mm. Pen and brown wash. Signed: *Pinelli fece 1817 Roma*.
No doubt made in emulation of David's celebrated picture of 1799.

A series of illustrations to the *Odes of Horace* were inserted as extra illustrations to the two volumes written and ornamented by Sir William Drummond and presented by him to King George IV in January 1828.

Pinelli's illustrations are in pen and grey ink and brown wash, measuring c.200×275 mm., on paper c.300×345 mm. The verse describing the incident depicted is inscribed in the margin at foot, and the drawings are signed *Pinelli fece Roma 1827*.

Vol. I.   Chariot race. Ode 1.
           The huntsman leaving his love. Ode 1.
           Venus and the maidens of Cytherea. Ode 4.
           Mercury guiding the souls to Elysium. Ode 10.
               This drawing is inscribed: *The idea of this drawing is taken from a picture by Fra Bartolomeo at Florence.*
           Paris and Helen in the ship. Ode 15.
           The punishment of the Centaurs. Ode 18.
           Drinking scene. Ode 27.
           The Chariot of Venus. Ode 30.

Vol. II. Book 2. The train of Bacchus. Ode 11.
           Sappho singing to a group of maidens. Ode 13.
           The Gods on Olympus; Sisyphus labouring. Ode 14.
           Bacchus teaching the nymphs. Ode 19.
           The death of the Giants. Ode 19.

See English Catalogue, s.v. Sir William Gell.

STEFANO POZZO
(c. 1707–1768)

The attribution of the following drawings is primarily based on Inventory A, which for artists as late as this is relatively reliable. Nos.712–14 are specifically attributed to him; Nos.719 and 720 come from a group of seven ascribed to Batoni and Pozzo, the other five being fairly clearly by Batoni. Nos.715, 717, and 718 come from a group mainly by Pietro de Pietri, but including five by pupils of Maratta, and No.716 from a series attributed to Pietro de Pietri, Masucci, and other followers of Maratta. The distinction between Pietro de Pietri and Pozzo is not always clear, but it is believed that the following drawings make a consistent group.

712. ST. JOACHIM AND ST. ANNE SEE A VISION OF THE VIRGIN IMMACULATELY CONCEIVED   (6735)
341 × 287 mm. Black and white chalk on grey-blue paper. Squared in white chalk.
A rare subject also treated by Guglielmo Cortese in a painting in S. Prassede, Rome.

Fig. 69   Cat. No. 713

713. THE VIRGIN AND CHILD IN GLORY (*Fig. 69*) (6734)
330 × 250 mm. Black and white chalk on grey-green paper.
The Christ Child stands at the Virgin's knee and tramples on the serpent.

714. THE NATIVITY WITH AN ADORING BISHOP (6736)
362 × 246 mm. Black and white chalk on grey-green paper.

715. A BISHOP BEFORE A ROMAN GOVERNOR   (5645)
341 × 301 mm. Black chalk.

716. MADONNA OF THE ROSARY WITH ST. DOMINIC AND A DOMINICAN NUN   (4428)
369 × 221 mm. Black and white chalk on grey-blue paper.

717. ST. CECILIA DISTRIBUTING ALMS   (5646)
331 × 287 mm. Black and white chalk on blue paper.
Based on Domenichino's fresco of the same subject in S. Luigi dei Francesi.

718. MINERVA   (5650)
380 × 132 mm. Black and white chalk on blue-grey paper.

719. HEAD OF A PHARISEE   (6730)
290 × 230 mm. Red chalk.
Probably a copy of a painting.

720. HEAD OF A ROMAN SOLDIER   (6727)
350 × 230 mm. Red chalk.
After a figure in Poussin's *Coriolanus*, now at Les Andelys.

ANDREA PROCACCINI
(1671–1734)

721. A WOMAN HOLDING A CLOTH   (01219)
574 × 415 mm. Red chalk on buff paper. Inscribed in the 'deceptive' hand: *Camilo Procaccini*.

Inventory A, p. 125: 'Camillo Procaccini, the Scholar of C. Maratti.'

Camillo Procaccini died in 1629, and the only artist of this name to be a pupil of Maratta was Andrea, to whom this drawing can therefore be ascribed.

MICHELANGELO RICCIOLINI
(1654–1715)

722. LANDSCAPE WITH A ROUND CHURCH AND AN AQUEDUCT   (3547)
201 × 310 mm. Pen and brown wash, with blue gouache.

The name of Ricciolini is written on the mount, but since no other landscapes by him are known, there is no means of checking the attribution.

723. LANDSCAPE WITH A RIVER   (0142)
192 × 301 mm. Pen and brown ink, black wash over black chalk.

The name of Ricciolini was written on the old mount.

Apparently by the same hand as No.722.

724. COPY AFTER RAPHAEL'S *DISPUTA*   (12070)
631 × 875 mm. Red chalk. Inscribed: *Raph : Vrb : In : & Pinx : In AEdib : Vatic : MARicciolinus del : A : 1759.*

The drawing shows the group of Popes and Bishops on the left of the altar.

GIOVANNI FRANCESCO ROMANELLI
(1610?–1662)

725. SOLOMON AND THE QUEEN OF SHEBA (?)   (4521)
    (Fig. 70)

196 × 263 mm. Pen and brown wash over black chalk.

Study for a painting in the *deposito* of the Capitoline Gallery traditionally ascribed to Romanelli.

Fig. 70   Cat. No. 725

This is one of the very few drawings which can be firmly attributed to the artist, but to it may be added the following which are in the same style and some of which have the artist's name inscribed in an eighteenth-century hand.

726. THE DEATH OF TURNUS   (0151)

202 × 296 mm. Pen and brown wash. Inscribed in the 'deceptive' hand: *Romaneli*.

Aeneas stabs Turnus, while Mercury hovers overhead.

727. CAMILLUS AND THE SCHOOLMASTER OF FALERII   (0150)

197 × 253 mm. Pen and brown wash over black chalk. Inscribed in the 'deceptive' hand: *Romanelli*.

Camillus, seated on the right, orders the treacherous schoolmaster to be led away bound, while the children kneel to thank him for his magnanimity.

728. CORIOLANUS   (0152)

197 × 253 mm. Pen and brown wash over black chalk.

Inv. A, p. 113, as Romanelli.

Coriolanus stands on the left, while his family kneels in supplication before him. This and Nos. 726 and 727 probably form part of a series illustrating ancient Roman history. If No. 725 represents Solomon and the Queen of Sheba, it evidently cannot belong to the series, but in format, style, and technique it is identical, and it may represent some story from classical history. The pyramids in the background suggest that it may take place in Egypt.

A painting of Coriolanus by Giuseppe Chiari at Burghley has many features in common with No. 728. Both may have a common origin in a lost drawing by Cortona.

729. THE SACRIFICE OF IPHIGENIA   (4522)

215 × 278 mm. Pen and brown wash, with traces of black chalk. Inscribed: *Sagrificio d'Ifigenia Figli[a] Agamenone Re de Micenis e di Clitemnestra. Val. Massimo lib. 8. cap. xi.*

Iphigenia kneels in the centre by an altar, while the executioner stands over her. Behind the altar stands the priest, to the left Agamemnon, shielding his face with his hand. In the right background the Greek fleet can be seen.

730. THE DEPARTURE OF A HERO   (0154)

225 × 313 mm. Pen and brown wash over black chalk. Inscribed: *Romanelli*.

A woman leads an armed hero towards the sea-shore, while soldiers follow carrying trunks and vases. The scene is not clearly identifiable, but may be Aeneas leaving Dido.

GIOVANNI FRANCESCO ROMANELLI
(attributed to)

731. MUTIUS SCAEVOLA   (4512)

220 × 388 mm. Pen and brown wash, heightened with white and blue gouache, on brown paper.

Inv. A, p. 111, as Pietro da Cortona.

732. THE GOLDEN CALF   (4511)

236 × 408 mm. Pen and brown wash, heightened with white and blue gouache, on brown paper.

Inv. A, p. 111, as Pietro da Cortona.

These two drawings, too feeble for Cortona, are different in technique from Nos. 725–30, but the types and the actual style of pen drawing seem to justify an attribution to Romanelli.

733. A SOLDIER RECEIVING THE SUBMISSION OF A YOUTH   (5986)

198 × 242 mm. Pen and brown wash, heightened with white, on discoloured white paper.

734. A MESSENGER SPEAKING TO A MAN SITTING AND DRINKING A CUP OF WINE   (6745)

183 × 195 mm. Pen and brown wash, heightened with white, over black, on blue-grey paper.

735. FLORA, CERES, BACCHUS AND (?) VERTUMNUS   (0155)

120 × 181 mm. Pen and brown wash, heightened with white.

736. DIANA AND AN ATTENDANT   (0156)

129 × 191 mm. Pen and brown wash, heightened with white.

By the same hand as No. 735.

CAMILLO RUSCONI
(1658–1728)

737. STATUE OF ST. MATTHEW (*Plate 66*)   (4168)

374 × 250 mm. Pen and brown ink, with grey wash, heightened with body-colour over black and some red chalk, on blue-grey paper.

From the Maratta volumes.

A study for the figure of St. Matthew in one of the niches of the nave-piers in St. John Lateran. The statue itself is in reverse, that is to say, with the right foot on the bag of money and the right knee supporting the book. This means that the figure, which is on the right-hand side of the nave, faces the altar. The present drawing was probably made when the figure was planned for a niche on the left of the nave.

CARLO RUSPI (active 1827)

Sir William Drummond's presentation copy, in two volumes of his *Odes of Horace*, given to King George IV in 1828, contains some 65 small drawings in pen and black ink of classical gems and fragments of sculpture. The great majority of them are very small, measuring 65 × 42 mm., and most are signed *C° Ruspi del*. In addition, others which are not signed are inscribed (probably by Sir William Drummond) *Done by Ruspi*. Several of Drummond's and Gell's decorations have been taken and enlarged from Ruspi's small drawings. The largest of Ruspi's drawings, and the only ones which contain more than one subject, are to be found in Volume I, between Odes 6 and 7 and show respectively the obverse and reverse of five and six Greek coins, probably life size. These drawings measure 150 × 240 mm. They have been inscribed with the names of the localities by Sir William Drummond. One of the smaller drawings, inserted at the beginning of Vol. I, is dated 1827 and signed. It is accompanied by a description in Carlo Ruspi's hand of a bust of Maecenas of which other variants are in the Capitoline Museum, in the collections of Prince Piombino, Prince Pugnatoschi, Prince Ennio Visconti and in the Museum at Naples. A similar inscription occurs at the foot of a sheet with a drawing of Augustus and his friends, a fragment of an ancient picture found in 1731 on the Palatine and at the time of writing in the collection of 'Chiaro Sigre. Mead Inglese'. There are some 65 drawings by Ruspi in the two volumes.

See *English Catalogue* s.v. William Gell.

ANDREA SACCHI
(1599–1661)

The drawings attributed to Sacchi in Inventory A were contained in two volumes and can be identified as Nos. 4854–4909 and 4921–4972, but to these were later added Nos. 4847–4853 and 4910–4920, which were inserted loose in the volumes from other sources. Generally speaking the old attributions have stood up well to the test of modern scholarship, though a certain number of drawings seem to have been moved from the Sacchi volumes into those devoted to Maratta and vice versa. This is not surprising, since the style of Maratta in his early years was close to that of his master, and he no doubt possessed the series of studies by Sacchi (Nos.745–760) for the *Destruction of Pagan Idols*, which he himself executed from them in the Lateran Baptistery. One might well assume that all the Sacchi drawings came with Maratta's collection into the possession of the Albani and so to the Royal Collection, but this is far from certain. There is even a passage in Bellori's life of Maratta which makes it actually improbable that this was their origin. According to the biographer, Sacchi at his death bequeathed many of his drawings to his pupils, but made one exception of Maratta, saying to him: 'It would not be right for me to leave my drawings to you, because you already know how to make your own to perfection. Be content therefore that these others who stand in need of them should have the benefit of them' (*Vite di Guido Reni, Andrea Sacchi e Carlo Maratti*, ed. Piacentini, Rome, 1942, p. 63). If this passage is to be taken literally, we must suppose that the drawings came by some other route, though it is always possible that Maratta may later have acquired drawings by Sacchi from one of the feebler pupils who benefited by them. Sacchi's drawings at Windsor have already been studied by H. Posse, who refers to them and reproduces a few in his monograph on the painter published in 1925. He did not, however, make any attempt to catalogue them, and further, since the publication of his book a number of new drawings have been discovered or identified. Some of these, such as *The Three Magdalens* (No.740), can be related to paintings of which the attribution was uncertain and which they help to confirm; but many others, though clearly by Sacchi, cannot at present be connected with any traceable composition. There is still room, however, for further research into the artist's paintings, which are no doubt to be found in the churches and collections of Italy, and into the problem of his designs for engravings or book-illustrations about which little is known. Another aspect of his work which is still totally obscure is his architecture, a field in which Bellori asserts that he was proficient, and with which a few drawings at Windsor are related.

1. Drawings connected with known works

BERLIN, Kaiser-Friedrich-Museum
THE DRUNKENNESS OF NOAH

Painted in the 1640's (cf. Posse, pp. 103 ff.).

738. STUDY FOR THE FIGURE OF NOAH   (4887)

367 × 450 mm. Red chalk. Inscribed: *disegno d'Andrea Sacchi copiato da Annibale Caracci*.

Verso: Study of a leg. Red chalk.

In spite of the inscription the drawing seems to be an original invention of Sacchi.

739. THE WHOLE COMPOSITION   (4858)

185 × 228 mm. Red chalk.

A copy after the painting. Other drawings for the composition are at Düsseldorf (Nos.67, 68) and in the Uffizi (cf. C. Refice, *Commentari*, i, 1950, p. 217, and Fig. 219).

Cf. also infra No.745.

FLORENCE, Cenacolo di S. Salvi
THE THREE MAGDALENS

A painting of this subject, apparently an altarpiece, was attributed to Sacchi by Professor Longhi, together with a small version in the Galleria Nazionale, Rome (cf. C. Refice, *Commentari*, i, 1950, p. 220). The latter was acquired from the Palazzo Chigi in Piazza Colonna. According to a verbal communication from the Marchese Giovanni Incisa della Rocchetta, kindly passed on by Professor Nolfo di Carpegna (who also supplied the information about the Florence picture), it appears in the Inventory of Cardinal Flavio Chigi, dating from 1692, as 'Le tre Maddalene, d'Andrea Sacchi.' The painting is described in detail by Bellori (*Vite di Guido Reni, Andrea Sacchi e Carlo Maratti*, ed. M. Piacentini, Rome, 1942, p. 67), who says that it was painted for Cardinal Antonio Barberini. He names the first two saints as St. Mary Magdalen and S. Maria Maddalena dei Pazzi; the last he describes as 'Sa. Madalena Regina dell' Indie, o sia della China'. The only persons who seem to fit this description are two Japanese women, both called Mary Magdalen, one Sanga, the other Kiota, who were martyred in the 1620's. These were in fact only beatified and not canonised, but Bellori is evidently somewhat vague about the whole identity of this character.

740. DRAWING FOR THE WHOLE COMPOSITION (*Fig. 71*) (4349)

429 × 300 mm. Red chalk and red wash on buff paper. Inscribed: *Andᵃ Sacchi*.

The drawing differs in several details from the painting. The poses of the two left-hand saints are slightly changed, and the lower part of the composition, with what appear to be river gods, is omitted in the painting.

Formerly OSTERLEY, Earl of Jersey Collection
AURORA

For the painting cf. F. H. Dowley, *Burlington Magazine*, ci, 1959, p. 68; repr. p. 69.

STUDIES FOR THE FIGURE OF AURORA

741. 171 × 234 mm. Red chalk and red wash.   (4872)

742. 160 × 181 mm. Red chalk and red wash.   (4172)

Lit.: Posse, *Sacchi*, p. 32.

No. 742 is from the Maratta volumes. The painting is traditionally ascribed to Maratta, as is the preliminary drawing for it in the Ambrosiana (cf. Dowley, *loc. cit.*). The two Windsor drawings cannot be by him and are probably the models by Sacchi on which Maratta based his painting. Posse points out the likeness of these drawings to certain figures in Albani's frescoes in the Palazzo Verospi.

Fig. 71   Cat. No. 740

Formerly PARIS, Orleans Collection
CHRIST CARRYING THE CROSS

743. STUDY OF A SOLDIER   (3608)

357 × 217 mm. Red chalk on buff paper.

Without traditional attribution, but on the analogy of certain other drawings by Sacchi at Windsor (*e.g.* No.763) almost certainly by him. The drawing is close to the figure of a soldier in the background of the Orleans picture and may be a study for it.

ROME, S. Carlo ai Catinari
THE DEATH OF ST. ANNE

Executed for S. Carlo ai Catinari, Rome, during the 1640's (cf. Posse, *op. cit.*, p. 95).

744. STUDY FOR THE WHOLE COMPOSITION   (4856)

189 × 127 mm. Pen and bistre.

Lit.: Posse, *op. cit.*, p. 96, and Pl. xvii.

ROME, S. Giovanni Laterano, Baptistery
THE DESTRUCTION OF PAGAN IDOLS

The painting was executed by Carlo Maratta after designs by Sacchi, as part of the redecoration of the Lateran Baptistery, probably about 1645-50. It is discussed and reproduced by Posse, *op. cit.*, pp. 84 f.

745. STUDIES FOR THE FIGURE OF THE PRIEST WITH
CRUCIFIX, ON THE LEFT   (4869)
235 × 333 mm. Red and white chalk on grey paper.
*Verso: Study for the two principal figures in the 'Drunkenness of
Noah'* (cf. Nos.738–39). Red chalk.
Lit.: Posse, *op. cit.*, p. 88.

746. STUDIES FOR THE HEAD AND HANDS OF THE
FIGURE WITH THE CRUCIFIX   (4863)
211 × 282 mm. Red chalk, touches of white, on grey paper.

747. STUDIES FOR THE HELMETED FIGURE TO RIGHT
OF CENTRE; A DRAPED FIGURE; AND OTHER STUDIES
                                               (4862)
281 × 332 mm. Red chalk, touches of white, on grey paper.
Lit.: Posse, *op. cit.*, p. 88.

748. STUDIES OF SHOULDERS AND HANDS FOR THE
SAME FIGURE   (4955)
198 × 306 mm. Red chalk, touches of white, on grey paper.

749. STUDIES FOR THE HEAD OF A MAN HOLDING A
STAFF   (4886)
227 × 180 mm. Red and white chalk on grey paper.

750. STUDIES FOR THE FIGURE HURLING A VASE, ON
THE RIGHT   (4921)
226 × 215 mm. Red and white chalk on grey paper.

751. STUDIES FOR THE HEAD AND TORSO OF THE SAME
FIGURE   (4860)
180 × 210 mm. Red and white chalk on grey paper.

752. STUDIES FOR THE HELMETED FIGURE IN THE RIGHT
BACKGROUND (*Fig. 72*)   (4959)
247 × 323 mm. Red chalk, heightened with white, on grey
paper.

753. SLIGHTER STUDIES FOR THE SAME FIGURE (4940)
210 × 177 mm. Red chalk, heightened with white, on grey
paper.

754. STUDIES OF ARMS, PROBABLY FOR THE SAME
FIGURE   (4926)
222 × 177 mm. Red chalk, touches of white, on grey paper.

755. STUDIES OF ARMS, PROBABLY FOR THE SAME
FIGURE; STUDIES FOR THE KNEELING FIGURE AT
CENTRE RIGHT   (4958)
243 × 343 mm. Cut on three sides. Red chalk, touches of
white, on grey paper.

756. STUDIES FOR THE BEARDED MAN ON THE EXTREME
RIGHT   (4923)
222 × 347 mm. Red chalk, a little white, on grey paper.

757. STUDIES OF AN OUTSTRETCHED ARM AND A POINT-
ING HAND   (4930)
245 × 180 mm. Black and white chalk on grey paper.

758. THREE FURTHER STUDIES OF HANDS   (4932)
237 × 175 mm. Black and white chalk on grey paper.

759. STUDIES OF A LEG AND A POINTING HAND   (4943)
264 × 176 mm. Black and white chalk on grey paper.

760. STUDIES OF PUTTI   (4867)
190 × 252 mm. Red chalks on white paper.
Lit.: Posse, *op. cit.*, p. 82.
Exh.: 17th Century Art, Royal Academy, London, 1938, No.
434.
This sketch is for the putti over the frescoes by Magnoni and
Camassei, and appears to have been finished by a pupil in
different coloured chalk.

ROME, S. Maria della Concezione
ST. ANTHONY REVIVING A DEAD MAN

Painting executed after 1631 for the Barberini (cf. Posse, *op.
cit.*, p. 60).

761. STUDY FOR THE WHOLE COMPOSITION   (4347)
260 × 188 mm. Red chalk and red wash on buff paper.
From the Maratta volumes.
Lit.: Posse, *op. cit.*, p. 60 and Pl. x.
A copy of this drawing is at Holkham. Another original
drawing for the whole design is at Düsseldorf (No.66).

762. STUDY FOR AN ONLOOKER   (4875)
160 × 143 mm. Red and white chalk on buff paper.
Lit.: Posse, *op. cit.*, p. 60.
Study for one of the onlookers on the left.

Fig. 72   Cat. No. 752

Fig. 73   Cat. No. 765

ROME, St. Peter's, Sala Capitolare
ST. ANDREW ADORING HIS CROSS

The painting was executed between 1633 and 1650 for the underground chapel at St. Peter's, and was later at Castel Gandolfo (reproduced in Posse, *op. cit.*, p. 57).

763. STUDY FOR THE FIGURE OF ST. ANDREW   (4934)
363 × 247 mm. Red chalk on buff paper.

Verso: Sketch for the kneeling figure in the centre of the 'Destruction of Pagan Idols' (cf. No. 745ff.).

ROME, Palazzo Barberini
ST. THOMAS AQUINAS WITH ST. PETER AND ST. PAUL

Cartoon for the mosaic in the pendentives of the Cappella della Madonna della Colonna in St. Peter's. The scheme was begun in 1624 (cf. Posse, *op. cit.*, p. 49).

764. STUDIES FOR THE HAND OF ST. THOMAS, HOLDING A BOOK   (4931)

170 × 257 mm. Black chalk on grey-brown paper.

Verso: Upper half of the figure of a bearded monk. Black chalk, heightened with white.

A drawing for the whole composition is at Düsseldorf (No. 65), and a copy of it is in a private collection in Rome (cf. C. Grassi, *Bernini Pittore*, Rome, 1944, Fig. 46).

The *verso* drawing bears some resemblance to the figure of St. Romualdus in the painting now in the Vatican Gallery, executed in the 1630's for the church of S. Romualdo, Rome (repr. Posse, *op. cit.*, Pl. xi).

ROME, Vatican Gallery
THE MASS OF ST. GREGORY

The painting was executed in 1625 for the Cappella Clementina in St. Peter's, and is now in the Vatican (reproduced in Posse, *op. cit.*, Pl. ix).

765. STUDY FOR THE WHOLE COMPOSITION   (4857)
161 × 122 mm. Red chalk, pen and bistre. *(Fig. 73)*
Lit.: Posse, *op. cit.*, p. 24.
Another sketch is in Berlin.

2. Drawings not connected with known works

766. ELIJAH ASCENDING TO HEAVEN *(Plate 28)*   (0183)
333 × 249 mm. Red chalk.

Without traditional attribution, but typical of Sacchi in style. The subject is rarely treated in the seventeenth century, except for the Order of Carmelites.

767. TOBIAS LEAVING HIS FAMILY *(Plate 25)*   (4095)
202 × 283 mm. Red chalk and red wash.

From the Maratta volumes, but certainly by Sacchi.

768. ST. FRANCIS AND OTHER SAINTS ADORING THE VIRGIN AND CHILD *(Plate 24)*   (4094)
211 × 312 mm. Red chalk and red wash.

From the Maratta volumes, but certainly by Sacchi.

St. Francis kneels before the Virgin and Child. Below, on the left, stands St. Peter with three other saints. In the centre kneel St. Gregory, St. Lawrence and others. To the right in the foreground sits St. Jerome.

769. DESIGN FOR A TITLE-PAGE, WITH THE ARMS OF CARDINAL LUDOVICO LUDOVISI *(Fig. 74)*   (4345)
261 × 174 mm. Red chalk. Illegible inscription in ink, probably approving the design for engraving. Incised with the stylus.

From the Maratta volumes, but certainly by Sacchi.

At the top a figure of Religion, holding the cross and the tiara, is adored by three worshippers. Below figures, presumably of unbelievers or heretics, flee in terror. In the centre two putti support the arms of the Cardinal. Below this is a space for an inscription, and at the bottom of the design are two putti with anchors. Presumably a design for a title-page.

770. AN ALLEGORY ON THE FOUNDATION OF ROME   (4175)

177 × 166 mm. Red chalk and red wash on buff paper.

From the Maratta volumes, but certainly by Sacchi.

Minerva stands holding a statuette apparently of Victory. At her feet Romulus and Remus are suckled by the wolf,

Fig. 74   Cat. No. 769

Fig. 75   Cat. No. 784

behind which is the figure of Tiber. In the distance the walls of Rome.

771. DANCE IN CASA FALCONIERI (*Fig. 76*)   (4864)

262 × 379 mm. Black chalk, pen and bistre.

Lit.: Posse, *op. cit.*, p. 8, and Pl. ii.

Exh.: 17th Century Art, Royal Academy, London, 1938, No. 435.

Engraved as plate 12 of *Relatione della famosa festa fatta in Roma alli 25 Febbraio 1634*, described by Cardinal Bentivoglio and published by Vitale Mascardi.

772. STUDIES OF CRIPPLES   (4865)

162 × 240 mm. Pen and bistre-wash.

Probably for a grotesque ballet or comedy.

773. STUDIES OF A MAN, HANDS AND FEET   (4942)

249 × 325 mm. Red and white chalk on buff paper.

The principal studies are for a man walking forward and making a gesture of surprise.

774. STUDIES OF A SHEPHERD   (4944)

222 × 322 mm. Red and white chalk on grey paper.

Possibly connected with the decorations at the Villa Sacchetti

at Castelfusano, which date from 1626–30 (cf. Posse, *op. cit.*, pp. 27 ff.).

775. A MAN WITH CYMBALS   (4279)

223 × 164 mm. Red chalk and red wash.

Lit.: Posse, *op. cit.*, pp. 34, 35 (repr.).

From the Maratta volumes.

Posse points out the general similarity of this drawing to the *Birth of Pindar* by Sacchi (repr. *op. cit.*, p. 33). An early work.

776. FIGURE OF A MAN   (4280)

265 × 115 mm. Red chalk.

From the Maratta volumes.

According to Inventory A (p. 108) this drawing is after Michelangelo. It does not seem, however, to be connected with any composition by him, though it may be a copy after some other sixteenth-century original. Probably an offset.

777. A DRAPED TORSO   (4391)

222 × 202 mm. Red chalk.

From the Maratta volumes.

The same statue as in Nos. 390 and 391, and very close in style to No. 391.

STUDIES OF HEADS

778. 130 × 109 mm. Black chalk. (4877b)

779. 136 × 139 mm. Black and white chalk on grey paper. (4878)

780. TWO ANCIENT HEADS (4885)
118 × 234 mm. Red chalk on buff paper. On two pieces of paper joined together.

781. PUTTI AND A GROTESQUE MASK (4866)
233 × 182 mm. Red chalk.

782. STUDIES OF DRAPERY, ETC. (4949)
252 × 158 mm. Black and white chalk on grey paper.

783. DESIGN FOR A CEILING DECORATION (4206)
192 × 249 mm. Red chalk.
From the Maratta volumes.

An all-over acanthus pattern, as in the Farnese Camerino, with oval and rectangular panels, round which are satyrs and dogs. Perhaps connected with the decoration of Castelfusano.

DESIGNS FOR AN ALTAR

784. 422 × 278 mm. Black chalk, touches of red chalk, brown washes, heightened with white. Inscribed with measurements in chalk and brown ink. (*Fig. 75*) (4970)

785. 112 × 288 mm. Black chalk and brown wash. (10893)
No.784 shows the whole altar with a niche containing a statue. No.785 shows the *mensa* only. In each case the *mensa* is decorated with the Barberini bees.

No architectural drawings are known which can with certainty be attributed to Sacchi, but the technique of No.784 is very close to drawings by him, such as No.786, and the architectural forms are in general like those in No.769. Bellori, moreover, particularly mentions Sacchi's competence in architectural matters and quotes his work for Cardinal Antonio Barberini at the Minerva (*Vite di Guido Reni, Andrea Sacchi e Carlo Maratti*, ed. M. Piacentini, Rome, 1942, p. 58) and the Lateran Baptistery (*ibid.*, p. 64). No. 784 comes from the Sacchi volumes, and both drawings may have been made in connection with one or other of these works.

786. DESIGN FOR A CARTOUCHE (4972)
195 × 195 mm. Black chalk, brown and grey wash and bodycolour, on grey paper.

According to Posse (*op. cit.*, p. 71) perhaps connected with the decoration of the Sacristy of S. Maria sopra Minerva, Rome.

Fig. 76   Cat. No. 771

Fig. 77   Cat. No. 788

DECORATIVE BORDERS FOR TAPESTRIES WITH THE
BARBERINI ARMS

787. 331 × 272 mm. Red and black chalk with water-colour.
(4855)

Exh.: 17th Century Art, Royal Academy, London, 1938, No.
436.

788. 254 × 208 mm. Red and black chalk with water-colour.
(*Fig. 77*)   (4854)

The Barberini archives show that Sacchi executed such
borders on at least two occasions, in 1639 and 1642 (cf.
Giovanni Incisa della Rocchetta, 'Notizie inedite su Andrea
Sacchi', *L'Arte*, xxvii, 1924, pp. 66, 69.

DESIGNS FOR THE DECORATION
OF A VAULT

Drawings Nos.789–820 are all for an important decorative
scheme, but it has hitherto proved impossible to relate them
to any recorded work by Sacchi. In many ways they answer
the description given by Bellori of his designs for the vault of
S. Luigi dei Francesi, which were only just begun at the time
of his death and were later destroyed (*Vite di Guido Reni,
Andrea Sacchi e Carlo Maratti*, ed. M. Piacentini, Rome, 1942,
p. 61), but the drawings would not fit the architecture of the
vault.

789. STUDY FOR A UNIT OF THE DECORATION   (4971)
235 × 305 mm. Black chalk on white paper.

Both seated and standing figures of the right-hand side are
shown, but only the standing figures on the left.

790. THE FIGURES OF THE LEFT-HAND SIDE   (4967)
269 × 130 mm. Red chalk on grey paper.

791. STUDY FOR THE UPPER PART OF THE LEFT-HAND
STANDING FIGURE   (4962)
300 × 225 mm. Red and white chalk on grey paper.
The figure is in the pose of Nos.789 and 790.

792. ANOTHER STUDY OF THE SAME FIGURE; TWO
DRAWINGS OF ARMS   (4906)
382 × 235 mm. Red and white chalk on grey paper.

793. STUDY FOR THE LEFT-HAND SEATED FIGURE,
ARMS EXTENDED   (4950)
228 × 158 mm. Red chalk, with touches of white, on grey
paper.

794. ANOTHER STUDY OF THE SAME FIGURE; SKETCH
OF THE LEFT LEG   (4927)
378 × 235 mm. Red chalk, touches of white, on grey paper.

795. THE SAME FIGURE, ON A SLIGHTLY LARGER SCALE
(4922)
387 × 222 mm. Red chalk, touches of white, on grey paper.

796. THE SAME FIGURE, IN A VARIANT POSE   (4963)
352 × 247 mm. Red chalk, touches of white, on grey paper.

797. SIX VARYING POSES FOR THE LEFT-HAND SEATED
FIGURE   (4938)
207 × 162 mm. Red chalk on white paper.

798. TWO STUDIES OF ONE OF THE VARIANT POSES
(4966)
368 × 232 mm. Red chalk, touches of white, on grey paper.

799. STUDY FOR THE LEFT-HAND GROUP, AN ALTER-
NATIVE ARRANGEMENT   (4969)
368 × 200 mm. Red chalk, heightened with white, on grey
paper.

800. STUDIES FOR THE LEFT-HAND SEATED FIGURE;
STUDY OF A HEAD   (4946)
248 × 352 mm. Red chalk, touches of white, on grey paper.

801. STUDIES FOR THE LEFT-HAND SEATED FIGURE;
SKETCH OF ARMS AND A FOOT   (4964)
375 × 235 mm. Red chalk, touches of white, on grey paper.

802. STUDY OF THE SEATED LEFT-HAND FIGURE AS
SHOWN IN NO. 801   (4939)
372 × 225 mm. Red chalk, heightened with white, on grey
paper.

803. THREE STUDIES OF A VARIANT FOR THE LEFT-
HAND SEATED FIGURE; FAINT SKETCHES FOR THE
CENTRE OF THE DECORATION, A SPHINX (cf. No.804),
AND THE RIGHT-HAND STANDING FIGURE   (4957)

159 × 203 mm. Red chalk on white paper.
Verso: Three further variants of Nos.795 and 798

804. TWO SKETCHES FOR THE CENTRAL AND RIGHT-
HAND SIDE OF THE DECORATIVE SCHEME: A SPHINX,
PUTTI, THE TORSO OF A TERM   (4861)
343 × 245 mm. Red chalk on grey paper.

805. THE FIGURES ON THE RIGHT, TERM AND SEATED
FIGURE (*Plate 27*)   (4941)
391 × 257 mm. Red chalk, heightened with white, on grey
paper. Measurements in P[iedi] and di[giti].
Lit.: Posse, *op. cit.*, p. 90.

806. THE RIGHT-HAND FIGURES IN A DIFFERENT POSE
197 × 127 mm. Pen on white paper.   (4871)

807. THE RIGHT-HAND FIGURES IN ANOTHER POSE
(*Fig. 78*)   (4870)
191 × 140 mm. Pen on white paper. Measurements and notes
in red chalk.

808. THE STANDING FIGURE ON THE RIGHT, THREE-
QUARTER LENGTH (*Plate 26*)   (4968)
308 × 219 mm. Red chalk, with touches of white, on grey
paper.
The pose is the same as in Nos.804 and 805.

809. THREE STUDIES OF THE UPPER PART OF THE
RIGHT-HAND STANDING FIGURE   (4937)
197 × 334 mm. Red chalk, heightened with white, on grey
paper.

810. THE UPPER PART OF THE RIGHT-HAND STANDING
FIGURE, HAND ON HEAD   (4884)
270 × 165 mm. Black and white chalk on grey paper.

811. THE UPPER PART OF THE RIGHT-HAND FIGURE,
LEANING LEFT   (4933)
261 × 188 mm. Black and white chalk on grey paper.

812. FIVE STUDIES FOR THE SEATED FIGURE ON THE
RIGHT; ONE OF THE LEFT SIDE OF THE SCHEME (cf. No.
801)   (4947)
260 × 334 mm. Red chalk on grey paper.

813. STUDY FOR THE RIGHT-HAND SEATED FIGURE;
SKETCH OF THE ARMS   (4952)
368 × 254 mm. Black chalk on grey paper, touches of white.

814. STUDY FOR THE RIGHT-HAND SEATED FIGURE IN
A VARIANT POSE   (4953)
375 × 242 mm. Black chalk on grey paper, heightened with
white.

815. THREE STUDIES FOR THE RIGHT-HAND SEATED
FIGURE; STUDY OF LEGS   (4925)
247 × 279 mm. Red and white chalk on grey paper.
The variant poses are as in Nos.812 and 816.

Fig. 78   Cat. No. 807

816. STUDY FOR THE RIGHT-HAND SEATED FIGURE
                                                 (4965)
228 × 190 mm. Red and white chalk on grey paper.

817. STUDY FOR THE RIGHT-HAND SEATED FIGURE
                                                 (4945)
359 × 216 mm. Red and white chalk on grey paper.

818. STUDY FOR THE RIGHT-HAND SEATED FIGURE
                                                 (4924)
362 × 229 mm. Black chalk, with touches of white, on grey
paper.

819. STUDY FOR THE RIGHT-HAND SEATED FIGURE
                                                 (4951)
330 × 242 mm. Black chalk, with touches of white, on grey
paper.
A variant of No.818.

820. STUDIES OF A NUDE   (4935)
232 × 315 mm. Red and white chalk on grey paper.
Though not directly connected with any of the above drawings, this has certain affinities to Nos.812 and 815 and may
be a preliminary sketch related to the scheme.

ACADEMIES

821. STANDING FIGURE, SUPPORTED ON RIGHT LEG, HOLDING A STAFF   (4848)
418×262 mm. Red chalk. Inscribed in ink: *De Andᵃ Sacch . .* (torn).

822. SEATED MALE ACADEMY FIGURE, FACING, LEFT HAND RAISED   (4851)
411×255 mm. Red chalk.
Loose in volume I of the Sacchi drawings, not accounted for in Inventory A.

823. STANDING MALE FIGURE, HOLDING A TORCH
404×257 mm. Red chalk.   (4852)
See note to No.822.

824. MALE NUDE FIGURE, SEATED, SUPPORTING A ROCK ON HIS SHOULDER   (4888)
565×370 mm. Red chalk, heightened with white. Inscribed (? in the 'deceptive hand' ?) : *Pittore Andrea Sacchi Romano.*

825. MALE FIGURE, SEEN FROM BEHIND, HOLDING A STAFF   (4889)
524×400 mm. Red chalk.
Verso : A seated figure supported on the right arm.

826. NUDE FIGURE OF A BOY LYING DOWN, LEANING ON A VASE   (4890)
281×378 mm. Red chalk, heightened with white.

827. MALE NUDE SEATED, THE LEFT LEG BENT AND RAISED   (4891)
375×265 mm. Red chalk, touches of white.

828. MALE NUDE SEATED, ARMS OUTSTRETCHED
                                                (4892)
333×245 mm. Red chalk. Unfinished.
Verso : Nude figure in a crouching position.

829. MALE NUDE STANDING, THREE-QUARTER LENGTH; STUDY FOR A SATYR   (4893)
308×201 mm. Red chalk.

830. A NUDE BOY SEATED, FACING HALF RIGHT   (4894)
378×220 mm. Red chalk.

831. YOUTH SEATED, TO LEFT, WITH ELBOW ON KNEE
348×213 mm. Red chalk.   (4895)

832. YOUTH STANDING, LEANING AGAINST A TREE, LEGS CROSSED   (4896)
400×218 mm. Red chalk.

833. STANDING MALE FIGURE, LEANING ON STAFF
                                                (4897)
388×229 mm. Red chalk, touches of white.

834. NUDE BOY SEATED, FACING HALF LEFT, HOLDING GRAPES   (4899)
383×262 mm. Red chalk, touches of white.

835. MALE NUDE FIGURE, SEATED, LEFT LEG BENT
353×245 mm. Red chalk, touches of white.   (4901)
Verso : Seated figure, seen from behind.

836. MALE NUDE FIGURE, SEATED TO RIGHT, LEFT LEG BENT   (4903)
345×243 mm. Red chalk, touches of white.

837. MALE NUDE FIGURE, SEATED, ONE ARM RAISED
388×233 mm. Red chalk, touches of white.   (4904)

838. STANDING MALE FIGURE, TO LEFT, LEANING ON A STAFF   (4907)
407×207 mm. Red chalk, touches of white (oxydised).

839. MALE FIGURE IN A CLOAK, LEANING FORWARD TO RIGHT, IN THE GESTURE OF HOLDING A STICK   (4913)
325×283 mm. Red chalk, touches of white.
Loose in volume II of the Sacchi drawings with Inventory Nos.4910–4920; not accounted for in Inventory A.

840. MALE FIGURE, FACING LEFT, RIGHT LEG AND LEFT ARM RAISED   (4915)
427×265 mm. Red chalk, faint touches of white.

841. STANDING MALE FIGURE, SUPPORTED ON LEFT LEG, HOLDING A STAFF   (4916)
409×268 mm. Red chalk, touches of white.

842. MALE NUDE FIGURE, SEATED, ONE FOOT RAISED
                                                (4917)
518×407 mm. Red chalk, heightened with white (oxydised).
Inscribed in black chalk at foot: *Andrea Sachi.*

843. MALE FIGURE, LYING DOWN   (4918)
410×538 mm. Red chalk, heightened with white (oxydised).
Inscribed in black chalk: *Andrea Sachi.*

844. MALE NUDE FIGURE, SEATED, RIGHT LEG RAISED AND EXTENDED   (4919)
424×523 mm. Red chalk, touches of white (oxydised).
Inscribed in black chalk: *Andrea Sachi.*

845. MALE NUDE FIGURE, SEATED, CLASPING HIS KNEE
                                                (4920)
355×458 mm. Red chalk, touches of white (oxydised).
Inscribed in black chalk: *Andrea Sachi.*

846. MALE NUDE FIGURE, STANDING, RIGHT ARM RAISED   (4928)

551 × 384 mm. Red chalk, touches of white.
Inscribed in ink: *And^a Sacchi*.

847. MALE NUDE FIGURE, STRIDING TO RIGHT   (4929)

511 × 354 mm. Red chalk.

848. MALE NUDE FIGURE, STANDING, TO RIGHT; STUDIES OF A HAND AND A LEG   (4936)

383 × 229 mm. Red chalk, touches of white (oxydised).

849. SEATED MALE FIGURE, TO RIGHT, HEAD TURNED AWAY   (4954)

367 × 251 mm. Black chalk on grey paper, touches of white.

850. SEATED MALE FIGURE WITH A HALO, FACING HALF LEFT; STUDY OF A HAND   (4956)

352 × 228 mm. Red chalk, touches of white.
Probably a pose-study for a St. Cecilia.

851. STANDING MALE NUDE, LEFT ARM RAISED; SEEN FROM BEHIND   (055)

420 × 240 mm. Red chalk.

3. Drawing after another artist

AFTER GUIDO RENI

852. CHRIST AT CALVARY   (4859)

342 × 214 mm. Red chalk. Inscribed: *Vien da Guido*.

A copy of the figure of Christ and one soldier in the painting by Guido at Schleissheim (repr. C. Gnudi, *Guido Reni*, Florence, 1955, Pl. 105).

ANDREA SACCHI
(attributed to)

853. A DISPUTATION ON THE HOLY SACRAMENT BEFORE URBAN VIII   (5203)

243 × 272 mm. Pen and brown wash.

Two ecclesiastics stand before the Pope, who sits surrounded by Cardinals. One of them points to a painting of the Host surrounded by clouds and cherubs' heads. The drawing is similar in general character to one at Ottawa (No.281), attributed to Cortona, but near to Sacchi, showing a female figure presenting a book to Urban VIII.
Both drawings were probably made to be engraved for illustrations to a book. Cf. also No.866.

854. A BATTLE SCENE   (4847)

191 × 214 mm. Red chalk.

A warrior running away from a battle faintly indicated in the distance is stopped by a woman sitting outside a tent, who by her gesture orders him back to the battle.
A feeble drawing, originally loose in the Sacchi volumes. Possibly a rather poor early original.

855. A KING   (4882)

394 × 235 mm. Black and white chalk on grey paper.

The figure of a king, crowned, standing with one arm outstretched. From the Sacchi series, but unlike him in style and probably by another member of the classicising group of artists working for the Barberini.

855a. A NYMPH, CENTAURS AND A LEOPARD   (4948)

333 × 226 mm. Black chalk, touched with white, on grey-blue paper.
Possibly after the Antique.

856. TWO FEMALE FIGURES   (5512)

210 × 168 mm. Red chalk.

Two seated women, one of whom puts her hand on the breast of the other and gazes into her eyes.
The subject may be Sappho.

857. A SLEEPING MALE NUDE   (4905)

221 × 350 mm. Drawn in black chalk and coloured with red, yellow and white chalk, on grey paper.

The use of coloured chalks is not usual with Sacchi, and they may be a later addition, but the actual draughtsmanship is very like his.

858. STUDY OF HANDS HOLDING A LEG   (0468)

147 × 242 mm. Red chalk.

859. NUDE STANDING FIGURE, SEEN FROM BEHIND   (4849)

310 × 195 mm. Black and white chalk on dark grey paper.
Loose in volume I of the Sacchi drawings, not accounted for in Inventory A.

860. A SEATED MALE NUDE, WITH ONE KNEE RAISED

400 × 247 mm. Red chalk.   (4850)

861. SEATED MALE NUDE, WITH HIS LEFT LEG RAISED

419 × 270 mm. Red chalk, heightened with white.   (4914)

862. SEATED MALE NUDE, HOLDING A STAFF   (4900)

406 × 266 mm. Red chalk.

863. MALE NUDE, SEATED ON A FRAGMENT OF AN ANCIENT ENTABLATURE   (5534)

402 × 556 mm. Red and white chalk on buff paper. Inscribed: *Cav.^e Bernini*.

In spite of the old inscription the drawing is far closer in style to Sacchi than to Bernini.

864. STANDING FEMALE FIGURE, SEEN FROM BEHIND   (4898)

433 × 267 mm. Red chalk, touches of white, on grey paper

865. HEAD OF A WOMAN   (4881)

200 × 170 mm. Black chalk on blue paper. Much damaged.

ANDREA SACCHI
(studio of)

866. A SEATED POPE   (3369)

376 × 230 mm. Black chalk with touches of white, on blue-grey paper.

A drawing without traditional attribution, but close in style to Sacchi's works of the 1630's. In its pose the nearest parallel is to be found in a drawing at Ottawa (No.281), referred to under No.853 above, which also shows a similar figure. In the form of the folds, however, the drawing comes very close to Carlo Pellegrini's cartoon of *St. Bernard*, made while he was working with Sacchi (repr. Posse, p. 53, Fig. 15). It also recalls in certain ways the style of Abbatini, as shown, for instance, in his frescoes in the Sacristy of S. Spirito in Sassia. The pope may be Urban VIII, but the identification is not certain.

867. CERES   (4876)

177 × 190 mm. Red chalk.

A figure seated in a spandrel. Probably a copy of a seventeenth-century fresco.

868. A WINGED CUPID   (4868)

155 × 299 mm. Red chalk.

Part of a decorative scheme, and probably a copy of a detail from a sixteenth-century fresco.

ANDREA SACCHI
(follower of)

869. STUDY OF A SEATED MALE NUDE   (882)

247 × 295 mm. Red chalk, on grey paper.

From the Domenichino volumes.

870. HEAD OF A MAN   (6738)

70 × 68 mm. Red chalk.

871. A MARTYR KNEELING BEFORE AN ALTAR   (5551)

215 × 163 mm. Red chalk and red wash.

The inscription on the back, only partly legible, is a fragment of a letter dated 1670.

From the Bernini volumes.

A priest kneels before an altar, while an angel hands him the palm of martyrdom, and on the right two men run away in terror. The technique is that of Sacchi, but the style is too emotional for him. It would on the other hand well fit with the date of 1670 suggested by the letter on the *verso*.

872. THE CRUCIFIXION WITH SAINTS   (6815)

363 × 227 mm. Red chalk and red wash.

At the foot of the Cross kneels a hermit; beside him stands a child carrying a disc with the letters *IHS*; to the right kneels a female Saint.

GIOVANNI BATTISTA SALVI
(called IL SASSOFERRATO)
(1609–85)

Drawings by this artist are excessively rare, and the Royal Collection is certainly unique in possessing more than sixty from his hand, thirty of which can be related to known paintings. The surprising fact is not that so many can be so related, but that so many remain unidentifiable, for almost every drawing in the group is a highly finished study, squared for transfer, and clearly made as a direct preparation for a painting. The explanation is that since the late nineteenth century Sassoferrato has been completely out of fashion as an artist, and no-one has taken the trouble to hunt out his paintings. The same might, of course, be said of many other artists represented in this volume, but in the case of Sassoferrato further and somewhat unexpected difficulties arise. The usual aids of engravings and early biographies with descriptions of paintings are not available. Sassoferrato seems to have worked almost exclusively for private patrons—there are only four paintings in Roman churches—and therefore did not attract the attention either of the critics or the engravers. Titi did not know his real name, and Mariette (*Abécédario*, v, p. 160) thinks it necessary to refute the view that he was a contemporary of Raphael. No doubt within the next few decades the rising taste for the Seicento will lead to the rediscovery of many paintings by this artist lurking in churches or private collections, but for the moment many of the drawings in the Royal Collection must remain unidentified as far as their destination is concerned.

Fortunately, from the point of view of their attribution, this is not a serious disadvantage. Sassoferrato's style is so uniform and so easily recognisable that there is rarely any doubt over the attribution of a drawing to him. Rarely, but not never. The Windsor series includes one drawing of the *Madonna and Child* (No.260) which agrees in every respect with the technique and manner of drawing shown in the rest of the group, though an acute observer noticed on seeing it that the sentiment was different. In fact it corresponds exactly to a painting by Maratta in Dresden and must, as far as one can judge, be a direct study for it. This discovery led to closer inspection of the whole series, and to the exclusion of the *St. Cecilia* (No.328) as being obviously similar to the *Madonna* both in feeling and in treatment, and to a query about the *Apollo* (No.936), which is like them, though not certainly by the same hand, and which incidentally had a place next to them in the eighteenth-century arrangement of the volume. Additional doubt is cast on the authenticity of this drawing by the fact that, as far as is known, Sassoferrato never painted a classical subject.

The series includes an important group of portrait drawings. Some of these are like Sassoferrato's religious drawings in technique and style, and two of them (Nos. 894 and 897) are studies for known portraits. But there are also five half life-size drawings of heads in coloured chalks quite unlike anything else associated with Sassoferrato, but which must be accepted as authentic because one of them is on the *verso* of an obviously genuine study of two figures for a religious subject.

1. Drawings connected with known works

BURGHLEY HOUSE, NORTHAMPTONSHIRE,
Marquis of Exeter Collection

THE MADONNA OF THE TOWER
Variant by Sassoferrato of Raphael's painting of that name (cf. No.897).

873. STUDY OF A CURTAIN   (6112)
396 × 273 mm. Black and white chalk on grey-brown paper. Squared.

Agrees, except in the form of the loop on the left, with the curtain in the painting.

DRESDEN, Gallery
THE MADONNA IN ADORATION
Reproduced in the 1929 catalogue, i, p. 430, No.432. Other versions are in the Vatican, at Bordeaux, and in the F. Hausmann collection, Berlin.

874. DRAWING FOR THE WHOLE FIGURE   (6058)
210 × 173 mm. Black and white chalk on grey-brown paper. Squared.

The Dresden version only shows the head and shoulders of the Virgin, whereas the drawing shows her at half-length.

FRANKFURT a/M, Städelsches Kunstinstitut
THE MADONNA
ADORING THE INFANT CHRIST
875. STUDY FOR THE MADONNA   (6059)
263 × 205 mm. Black and white chalk on grey-green paper. Squared.

876. STUDIES FOR THE HEAD AND HANDS OF THE MADONNA   (6050)
167 × 201 mm. Black and white chalk on grey-green paper. Squared.

877. STUDY FOR THE HEAD AND SHOULDERS OF THE MADONNA (*Plate 31*)   (6053)
210 × 172 mm. Black and white chalk on green-grey paper. Squared.

HIGHNAM COURT, GLOUCESTER,
Gambier-Parry Collection
THE MADONNA IN PRAYER
878. STUDY FOR THE WHOLE COMPOSITION   (6047)
153 × 172 mm. Black and white chalk. Squared.

LONDON, Wallace Collection
THE MARRIAGE OF ST. CATHERINE
879. STUDY FOR THE WHOLE COMPOSITION (*Plate 29*)
                                             (6084)
422 × 274 mm. Black and white chalk on grey-brown paper. Squared. Inscribed in top left-hand corner: *59*.

Formerly LONDON, with Leger Galleries
MADONNA IN PRAYER
Reproduced in *Pantheon* for May 1928 as an advertisement.

880. STUDIES FOR THE HEAD AND SHOULDERS OF THE MADONNA   (6054)
267 × 181 mm. Red, black and white chalk on grey-brown paper. Squared.

MILAN, Brera
THE IMMACULATA
Another version of the painting is in the Louvre.

881. STUDY FOR THE FIGURE OF THE VIRGIN   (6073)
318 × 186 mm. Black and white chalk on grey-brown paper. Squared in red chalk.

NAPLES, Museo Nazionale
THE NATIVITY
Reproduced in Voss, p. 220.

882. STUDY FOR THE VIRGIN (*Plate 33*)   (6065)
303 × 235 mm. Black and white chalk on grey-green paper. Squared.

883. STUDY FOR ST. JOSEPH AND THE CHRIST CHILD
                                             (6066)
343 × 200 mm. Black and white chalk on grey-green paper. Squared.

STUDIES FOR THE CHRIST CHILD
884. 111 × 186 mm. Black and white chalk on grey-green paper. Squared.   (6049)

885. 110 × 172 mm. Black chalk squeeze drawing on blue-grey paper. Squared.   (6082)

These two drawings show the Child in a slightly different pose from the painting, but must nevertheless be studies for it.

PERUGIA, St. Pietro
THE MADONNA AND CHILD
886. STUDY FOR THE WHOLE COMPOSITION   (6067)
388 × 243 mm. Black and white chalk on grey-blue paper. Squared.

The drawing shows additional studies of the Virgin's head and right hand. A red chalk drawing in an album at Saltram (Devon), belonging to the National Trust, is probably a preliminary study for this composition.

Fig. 79   Cat. No. 887

PERUGIA, St. Pietro
COPIES OF BUSTS OF ST. FLAVIA, ST. APOLLONIA AND ST. CATHERINE

Copies after Perugino, presumably made when the originals, now in the Vatican, were removed (repr. *Klassiker der Kunst*, 1914, Pls. 63 ff.).

887. ST. FLAVIA (*Fig. 79*)
192 × 162 mm. Black and white chalk on grey-green paper. Squared.   (6063)
Lit.: Reproduced in the *Jahrbuch der Bibliothek Hertziana*, i, 1937, p. 255.
Exact copy of Perugino's original, to which, in his painted copy, Sassoferrato has added a crown.

ROME, S. Giovanni in Laterano, Baptistery, Cappella di S. Rufina
MADONNA AND CHILD WITH ST. JOHN

888. STUDY FOR THE WHOLE COMPOSITION (*Plate 30*)
                                                        (6095)
303 × 263 mm. Black and white chalk on grey-blue paper. Squared.
A drawing of this composition without the figure of St. John is in the Ashmolean (No.944).

ROME, S. Sabina
THE MADONNA OF THE ROSARY

Painted in 1643 (cf. Waterhouse, p. 94; repr. Voss, p. 214).
889. STUDY FOR THE WHOLE COMPOSITION   (6087)
146 × 115 mm. Black chalk. Squared in red chalk.

890 STUDY FOR THE MADONNA AND CHILD   (6088)
284 × 206 mm. Black and white chalk on grey-green paper. Squared.

891. STUDY FOR THE KNEELING FIGURE OF ST. CATHERINE OF SIENA   (6074)
264 × 190 mm. Black and white chalk on grey-green paper. Squared.
A drawing for the St. Dominic is in the Ashmolean (No.943).

Formerly ROME, Lucien Bonaparte Collection
HOLY FAMILY

The composition is closely based on Raphael's Canigiani *Holy Family*.

892. STUDY FOR THE WHOLE COMPOSITION   (6080)
385 × 404 mm. Black and white chalk on grey-green paper. Squared.

ROME, Doria Gallery
HOLY FAMILY

893. THE SLEEPING CHRIST CHILD   (6052)
208 × 140 mm. Black and white chalk on grey-green paper.

ROME, Galleria Nazionale
PORTRAIT OF MONSIGNOR OTTAVIANO PRATI

The painting bears the names of both the artist and the sitter.

894. STUDY FOR THE WHOLE COMPOSITION   (6105)
262 × 194 mm. Black and white chalk on grey-green paper. Squared.

ROME, Private Collection
THE MADONNA IN PRAYER

Painting known through a photograph in the Gabinetto Nazionale (No.6504).

895. STUDY FOR THE WHOLE COMPOSITION, WITH DETAIL-STUDY OF THE ARMS   (6064)
318 × 218 mm. Black and white chalk on brown-tinted paper.

896. STUDY FOR THE HANDS ONLY (*Fig. 80*)   (6055)
323 × 246 mm. Black and white chalk on grey-brown paper.
The hands are closely based on Perugino's *St. Flavia* (cf. No. 887).

SARASOTA, Ringling Museum
PORTRAIT OF A CARDINAL

In the background hangs a painting of the *Madonna and Child*, which was executed by Sassoferrato in close imitation of Raphael's *Madonna of the Tower*, and is now at Burghley House. No doubt it was painted for the sitter, but as nothing is known of the history of the *Madonna* the identity of the sitter cannot be determined.

897. STUDY FOR THE PRINCIPAL FIGURE AND DETAIL OF HANDS (*Plate 35*)   (6102)

381 × 227 mm. Black and white chalk on grey-green paper. Squared.

Exh.: 17th Century Art, Royal Academy, London, 1938, No. 412.

URBINO, Galleria Nazionale
CRUCIFIXION

Reproduced in the *Bollettino d'Arte*, i, 1921, p. 280.

898. STUDY FOR THE WHOLE COMPOSITION (*Fig. 81*)   (6093)

262 × 182 mm. Black chalk. Squared, partly in red chalk, except for the figure of Christ.

The drawing differs from the painting in showing two angels kneeling symmetrically at the foot of the Cross and two putti flying above them, whereas the painting has one angel only, on the left, and St. John on the right. It is, therefore, possible that the drawing may be a preparation for another painting now lost (Thieme-Becker records a signed *Crucifixion* formerly in the Weber collection, Hamburg), but the existence of a study for the mourning St. John (No.901) seems to confirm the hypothesis that the two are connected.

899. STUDY FOR THE LEFT-HAND ANGEL (*Plate 32*)   (6072)

350 × 253 mm. Black and white chalk on grey-brown paper. Squared.

This corresponds exactly with the painting.

Fig. 81   Cat. No. 898

900. STUDY FOR THE RIGHT-HAND ANGEL   (6070)

365 × 233 mm. Black and white chalk on grey-brown paper. Squared.

901. STUDY FOR ST. JOHN (*Fig. 83*)   (6060)

212 × 132 mm. Black and white chalk on grey-green paper. Squared.

This drawing shows him facing right, so that, if it is connected with the Urbino painting, Sassoferrato must at one stage have planned to have the angel on the right and St. John on the left.

THE ANNUNCIATION

Painting known from a photograph among the Richter archives in the National Gallery, Washington.

902. STUDY FOR THE ANGEL (*Fig. 86*)   (6048)

208 × 178 mm. Black and white chalk. Squared.

2. Drawings not connected with known works

903. JUDITH WITH THE HEAD OF HOLOFERNES (*Plate 36*)   (6078)

372 × 255 mm. Black and white chalk on blue-grey paper. Squared.

Fig. 80   Cat. No. 896

Fig. 82   Cat. No. 905

Exh.: 17th Century Art, Royal Academy, London, 1938, No. 407; Royal Academy, London, 1950–51, No.439.

904. THE ANNUNCIATION (*Fig. 84*)   (6092)

317 × 265 mm. Black and white chalk on grey-green paper.

The Virgin stands full-face and at full-length on the right; the angel kneels on the left, almost in profile. Above the angel are two figures with halos, not apparently connected with the main subject. Above the angel are two heads.

905. THE ANNUNCIATION (*Fig. 82*)   (6094)

398 × 270 mm. Black and white chalk on grey-green paper. Squared.

Verso: St. Joseph carrying the Christ Child.

The *recto* drawing, which consists of a drawing of the whole composition, two details of the Virgin's head and one of the angel's head, is clearly copied from a painting of the early fifteenth century which has not, however, been identified.

906. THE MADONNA AND CHILD   (6056)

238 × 237 mm. Black and white chalk on grey-green paper. Squared. Inscribed: *34*.

Half-length study of the Madonna holding the naked Christ Child, who stretches out his arms towards her.

907. THE MADONNA, STANDING AT WHOLE-LENGTH AND HOLDING THE CHILD WHO GIVES THE BLESSING (*Fig. 85*)   (6075)

244 × 157 mm. Black and white chalk on grey-brown paper. Squared.

908. MADONNA AND CHILD WITH ST. CATHERINE AND ST. BARBARA   (6085)

257 × 194 mm. Black and white chalk on grey-green paper. Squared.

No painting is known which exactly corresponds, but one, containing all the figures except St. Barbara in half-lengths, formerly belonged to Fairfax Murray.

909. STUDY FOR ST. BARBARA   (6071)

374 × 246 mm. Black and white chalk on grey-brown paper. Squared. Inscribed in the top right-hand corner: *misura del naturale*.

The Saint is shown facing half right, whereas in No.908 she faces half left, but in spite of this the drawing is probably a preliminary study for the composition.

910. HEADS OF THE MADONNA AND CHILD   (6046)

226 × 278 mm. Black and white chalk on grey-green paper. Squared.

Both seen almost full-face. Christ is shown as a child, not as a baby.

911. THE VIRGIN, CHILD, AND ST. JOSEPH (*Fig. 87*)   (6057)

245 × 200 mm. Black and white chalk on grey-brown paper. Squared.

Half-length. The Child kisses the Virgin; St. Joseph looks over her shoulder.

912. THE VIRGIN UNVEILS THE SLEEPING CHRIST CHILD (*Fig. 88*)   (6083)

190 × 173 mm. Black and white chalk on green-grey paper. Squared.

The Virgin, facing left, lifts a veil from the Child, who is asleep with his head to the left. On the right stands St. Joseph, looking over her shoulder. The iconography goes back to a lost painting by Raphael known in many copies.

913. THE HOLY FAMILY   (6081)

264 × 332 mm. Black and white chalk on grey-brown paper. Squared.

The Virgin is about to take from St. Joseph the Child, who stretches out his arms towards her.

914. THE VIRGIN, CHILD, AND ST. JOHN (*Fig. 89*) (6091)

317 × 233 mm. Black and white chalk on green-grey paper. Squared.

The Virgin sits full-face. Christ stands on the right, stretching out his hands towards St. John, who stands on the left.

Fig. 83   Cat. No. 901   Fig. 84   Cat. No. 904   Fig. 85   Cat. No. 907

Fig. 86   Cat. No. 902   Fig. 87   Cat. No. 911   Fig. 88   Cat. No. 912

Fig. 89   Cat. No. 914   Fig. 90   Cat. No. 917   Fig. 91   Cat. No. 920

Fig. 92 Cat. No. 916 Fig. 93 Cat. No. 921 Fig. 94 Cat. No. 922 Fig. 95 Cat. No. 923

915. THE CHRIST CHILD ASLEEP (6061)

148 × 158 mm. Black and white chalk on grey-blue paper. Squared.

916. ST. JOSEPH HOLDING THE CHRIST CHILD (6079)

378 × 219 mm. Black and white chalk on blue-grey paper. Squared. (*Fig. 92*)

St. Joseph, at full-length, stands carrying on his right arm the Child, who lays his hand on an orb which St. Joseph holds in his left hand.

917. GOD THE FATHER SUPPORTING THE DEAD CHRIST (*Fig. 90*) (6090)

307 × 242 mm. Black and white chalk on blue-grey paper. Squared in red and black chalk. Inscribed: *49*.

918. ST. ANTHONY ABBOT (*Plate 37*) (6069)

249 × 179 mm. Black and white chalk on green-grey paper. Squared.

Kneeling, facing right, accompanied by his pig.

919. ST. ANTHONY OF PADUA (6086)

123 × 94 mm. Black chalk. Squared. An ink inscription on the *verso* (laid down).

Seated, full-face and at half-length, with the Christ Child on the table at which he sits.

920. STUDIES FOR THE ST. ANTHONY OF PADUA (6089)

265 × 203 mm. Black and white chalk on grey-brown paper. Inscribed: *62*. (*Fig. 91*)

The main sketch shows the Saint seated, facing right,

Fig. 96 Cat. No. 924 Fig. 97 Cat. No. 925 Fig. 98 Cat. No. 927

reading at a desk, with the Christ Child who appears to him, carrying the orb and standing on the book which he has been reading.

921. ST. LAWRENCE AND A BISHOP (*Fig. 93*)   (6068)
391 × 249 mm. Black and white chalk on green-grey paper. Squared.

Verso: Portrait head. Black, brown, red and white chalks.

The *recto* shows the two figures at full length, nearly full-face. for the *verso* see the note to Nos. 929–932.

922. ST. MARGARET (*Fig. 94*)   (6077)
396 × 245 mm. Black and white chalk on grey-brown paper. Squared.

The Saint stands full-face and at full-length, with one foot on the figure of Satan.

923. ST. MARY MAGDALENE AT THE FOOT OF THE CROSS (*Fig. 95*)   (6076)
387 × 243 mm. Black and white chalk on grey-green paper. Squared.

Verso: Standing figure of a woman.

Kneeling, facing left, with both hands on the Cross. The drawing on the *verso* is probably for the Virgin at the foot of the Cross for the same composition.

924. PORTRAIT OF AN ECCLESIASTIC (*Fig. 96*)   (6103)
357 × 254 mm. Black and white chalk on grey-brown paper. Squared.

Full-length, seated, facing slightly left and holding a biretta. Behind, on the left, indications of an altar with a painting hung over it, as in the portrait at Sarasota (cf. No.897).

925. PORTRAIT OF AN ECCLESIASTIC (*Fig. 97*)   (6104)
383 × 243 mm. Black and white chalk on grey-brown paper. Squared.

Standing full-length, with his hand on a book and wearing a biretta.

926. PORTRAIT OF AN ECCLESIASTIC (*Plate 34*)   (6100)
269 × 204 mm. Black and white chalk on grey-green paper. Squared.

Exh.: Royal Academy, London, 1950–51, No.438.
Seated at a table, with his hand on an open book.

927. HEAD AND SHOULDERS OF AN ECCLESIASTIC (*Fig. 98*)   (6106)
258 × 191 mm. Black and white chalk on grey-green paper. Bald, and wearing an ecclesiastical tippet.

928. PORTRAIT OF A MONK   (6101)
388 × 227 mm. Black and white chalk on grey-green paper.
One study at half-length, with the head and hands fully drawn and the habit only sketched in; another of the habit and hood, without head; one of the hood only; and one of the hands.

929. HEAD OF A CARDINAL (*Plate 38*)   (6111)
346 × 259 mm. Black, brown, red, and white chalk on grey-green paper.

930. HEAD OF A MAN   (6108)
350 × 239 mm. Black, brown, red, and white chalk on grey-green paper.

931. HEAD OF A MAN WITH LONG HAIR (*Plate 39*)   (6109)
364 × 259 mm. Black, brown, red, and white chalk on grey-green paper.

932. HEAD OF A WOMAN   (6110)
350 × 254 mm. Black, brown, red, and white chalk on grey-green paper.

These four portrait heads are quite unlike anything known by Sassoferrato either in style or technique, but the traditional attribution to him is confirmed by the drawing on the *verso* of No.921, the *recto* of which is obviously by him.

GIOVANNI BATTISTA SALVI
(called IL SASSOFERRATO)
(attributed to)

933. HEAD OF A YOUTH AND STUDIES OF A HAND ON A SMALLER SCALE   (6107)
373 × 257 mm. Black and white chalk on grey-green paper.
Traditionally attributed to Sassoferrato, but not quite like the other portraits in style. It may, however, be by the same artist working at a slightly different period.

934. PORTRAIT OF A GIRL CARRYING A MUFF, AND HEAD OF A YOUTH   (6099)
372 × 272 mm. Black and white chalk on grey-brown paper. Squared. In the top left-hand corner is inserted, on a separate sheet of paper, a *Head of a Youth:* 131 × 101 mm. Black chalk.

Exh.: Burlington Fine Arts Club, London, 1925, No.24; *17th Century Art*, Royal Academy, London, 1938, No.408.

The costume of the girl is, as Mrs. Eric Newton kindly informed me, almost certainly not Italian, but more probably Dutch or Flemish. The drawing, however, is very close to the portraits by Sassoferrato in style, and in view of this fact and of the traditional attribution, it has been left with them, though an element of doubt subsists. It is, of course, possible that Sassoferrato should have drawn a Dutch woman visiting Rome.

GIOVANNI BATTISTA SALVI
(called IL SASSOFERRATO)
(after)
FRANKFURT a/M, Städelsches Kunstinstitut
MADONNA IN PRAYER

935. COPY OF THE WHOLE COMPOSITION   (4424)
178 × 125 mm. Black and red chalks.

Inv. A, p. 110: From the volume containing works by Pietro di Pietri, Masucci and Stefano Pozzo.

The copy seems to date from the early eighteenth century, and to have been made by a follower of Maratta, probably Pietro de Pietri.

GIOVANNI BATTISTA SALVI
(called IL SASSOFERRATO)
(follower of)

936. APOLLO   (6098)

329×272 mm. Black and white chalk on grey-blue paper. Traditionally ascribed to Sassoferrato, but different in subject and feeling from his normal work, though similar in technique. The drawing is close to the two drawings hitherto attributed to Sassoferrato but actually by Maratta, and may possibly be an early work by him (cf. Nos.260, 328).

GIOVANNI PAOLO SCHOR
(1615–74)

A large group of drawings with traditional attributions to Bernini or Pietro da Cortona can be assigned with a high degree of probability to the studio of the Tyrolese artist Giovanni Paolo Schor, who worked under Cortona in the Quirinal for Alexander VII and under Bernini on the Cathedra Petri (cf. R. Battaglia, *La Cattedra Berniniana di S. Pietro*, Rome, 1943, *passim*). For the most recent and complete account of the Schor family see Gertrude Aurenhammer, *Die Handzeichnungen des 17ten Jahrhunderts in Oesterreich*, Vienna, 1958.

The usual basis for attributions to Schor is the series of drawings in the Corsini, with his name written on many of them in an old hand. These drawings were first noticed by Brauer and Wittkower (*op. cit.*, p. 8 note 7), who also called attention to the existence of others at Windsor, and attributed to Schor certain sketches reproduced by Fraschetti (*Il Bernini*, Milan, 1900, pp. 118, 172, 228) as the work of Bernini. One Corsini drawing is reproduced in Aurenhammer (*op. cit.*, pl. 1), and two in Battaglia (*op. cit.*, Pl. xxiii). These are all very free sketches for decorative motives—frames, coaches, monstrances, etc.—in a style that is readily recognisable. Other drawings in the same manner and also bearing old attributions to Schor are in the British Museum (1946–7–13–819 and 1952–1–21–16) and in an album of drawings belonging to the National Trust at Saltram, Devon. A number of the drawings listed below can be connected with this group, in some cases on general grounds of style, but in one instance because a design for the same coach is among the inscribed drawings in the Corsini.

There is, however, at Windsor one drawing of a quite different kind, which makes it possible to connect a further group with the name of Schor. This drawing, No.937), is a direct preparation for Schor's painting of *Noah watching the animals going into the Ark*, executed for Alexander VII in 1656–57 (cf. Aurenhammer, *op. cit.*, pp. 13 ff.). It is highly finished and in a marked style characterised by a somewhat fussy pen line with light bistre ink, and extensive use of grey wash. Exactly the same style and technique are to be found in three large drawings for a decorative scheme (Nos.940–942), also for Alexander VII. To these can be added two roundels

representing the story of the Prodigal Son (Nos.938, 939); two drawings of the decoration of St. Peter's for the Canonisation of St. Thomas of Villanueva in 1658 (Nos.943, 944); a fantastic design for a clock (No.946), one for an altar (No.945), and two for salt cellars (Nos. 947, 948).

The manner of these drawings is so different from the known sketches of G. P. Schor that one is led to wonder whether they are by a studio hand, perhaps, for instance, his brother Egid, who worked with him at the Quirinal, but went back to Innsbruck about 1665. One of his drawings in Berlin (repr. Aurenhammer, *op. cit.*, Pl. 7) is very like the design for a clock at Windsor.

As regards the designs for coaches, of which three exist at Windsor, the names of Ferri and G. B. Lenardi have also been suggested, but the attribution to Schor is established by the existence of the drawing in the Corsini referred to above. Even without this clue, however, the name of Ferri would not have been acceptable, for his style of coach-design, as it is known for instance from a drawing at Düsseldorf (No.254) and from the plates to *Lord Castlemaine's Embassy* of 1688, is entirely different and much less Baroque. As far as can be ascertained, Lenardi only comes into the story as the man who made the drawings for the engravings in *Castlemaine's Embassy* —and probably for other books—but he does not seem to have invented decorative designs of this kind at all. According to Thieme-Becker he is not the same as G. B. Lenardi known through a few drawings and engraved compositions (cf. above, No.250), which certainly have nothing in common with the engraved coach designs.

937. NOAH WATCHING THE ANIMALS GOING INTO THE ARK (*Fig. 99*)   (4513)

176×440 mm. Pen and brown ink, with grey wash and touch of white body-colour.

Finished preparation for the painting executed in 1656–7 for the Gallery of the Quirinal on the orders of Alexander VII (cf. Aurenhammer, *op. cit.*, pp. 13 ff.). The drawing differs in too many details for it to be a copy after the painting, but must rather be the immediate preparation for it.

938. THE DEPARTURE OF THE PRODIGAL SON   (4543)

Circular. 340 mm. in diameter. Pen and brown ink, grey wash. Damaged and patched.

939. THE PRODIGAL SON WASTING HIS SUBSTANCE IN RIOTOUS LIVING   (4542)

Circular. 340 mm. in diameter. Pen and brown ink, with grey wash, retouched with grey gouache and lead pencil.

STUDIES FOR A DECORATIVE SCHEME FOR ALEXANDER VII

940. 424×367 mm. Pen and black ink, with black and reddish-brown wash, on faded white paper.   (4443)

941. 417×355 mm. Pen and black wash, on faded white paper.   (4445)

942. 432×366 mm. Pen and black wash, touched with white, on faded white paper.   (4444)

These three drawings show alternatives for the decoration of a room with the wall-space covered with cupboards, perhaps a library or a treasury. The arms of Alexander VII are prominently displayed, and in various small panels are views of the palace and church at Castel Gandolfo.

943. SECTION OF THE NAVE OF ST. PETER'S   (11594)

407×618 mm. Pen and brown ink, with grey wash, on discoloured white paper. A scale at the bottom.

944. SECTION OF THE DOME AND TRANSEPT OF ST. PETER'S   (11595)

408×609 mm. Pen and brown ink, with grey and brown wash and touches of water-colour, on discoloured white paper.

The drawings show St. Peter's decorated for a special occasion, and Dr. Arnold Noach has identified this as the canonisation of St. Thomas of Villanueva in 1658. The decoration agrees with the descriptions given in the *Breva Relazione*, published in Rome and Florence in 1658, and the *Breve Relación*, published in Valencia in 1659.

The decorations show the pilasters of the nave covered with damask, and between the pairs of pilasters the arms of Alexander VII and the King of Spain. In the arches are hung medallions with scenes from the life of the Saint.

945. DESIGN FOR AN ALTAR   (5598)

415×284 mm. Pen and brown ink, with blue-grey wash. A scale at the bottom.

The design shows a baldacchino composed of four Salomonic columns like those of St. Peter's. At the top putti carry the Crown of Thorns, and an angel holds the Cross.

The architectural style is that of Bernini, but the draughtsmanship is that of the group of finished drawings ascribed to the studio of G. P. Schor.

946. DESIGN FOR A CLOCK (repr. p. 12)   (4442)

484×327 mm. Pen and black wash on faded white paper.

A fantastic design, showing a sorceress, perhaps Medea, driving in her dragon-drawn chariot, against a background of ruined columns. The general scheme recalls the fountain in the Palazzo Borghese, designed by Schor in 1672 (cf. E. Rossi, 'Cronache e documenti di vita Romana', *Roma*, 1942, p. 295) and an account of a room designed by him in the Palazzo Altieri (cf. above, p. 9).

DESIGNS FOR SALT CELLARS

947. 268×133 mm. Torn in the two upper corners. Pen and black wash.   (4457)

948. 130×201 mm. Torn in the top left-hand corner. Black chalk and black wash.   (4469)

No.947 shows a bowl supported by mermaids; in No.948 the bowl is carried by three putti and flanked by Minerva and Hercules.

949. THE ARMS OF POPE CLEMENT X (repr. p. 193) (4441)

386×267 mm. Pen and brown ink, with brown wash and water-colour. An illegible inscription at foot.

Perhaps a design for a tapestry. The technique is like that of the preceding drawings, except for the use of water-colour, but the drawing is freer. Presumably made between the accession of Clement X in 1670 and the death of G. P. Schor in 1674.

950. DESIGN FOR A DOOR WITH THE COLONNA ARMS   (5592)

220×229 mm. Pen and black ink, with black wash and water-colour.

The design shows a round-headed arch closed by an open-work metal gate and flanked by two small square-headed doors. Over the arch are the arms of Colonna, surmounted by what appears to be a coronet of a Prince of the Empire. Very close in style and technique to No.949.

Fig. 99   Cat. No. 937

Fig. 100   Cat. No. 956

Fig. 101   Cat. No. 962

DESIGNS FOR COACHES

951. DESIGN WITH ALLEGORICAL FIGURES OF FAITH, FORTITUDE AND TRUTH (*Plate 46*)   (4462)

212 × 192 mm. Pen and brown wash over black chalk.

A design for the back of the same coach, with small variations in the figure of Faith, is in the Corsini (repr. Aurenhammer, *op. cit.*, Pl. 1), with an early inscription giving it to Schor.

952. DESIGN FOR THE BACK OF A COACH WITH A VICTORIOUS WARRIOR (*Plate 45*)   (4461)

252 × 209 mm. Pen and brown wash over black chalk.

A figure in armour, with a sun on his shield and accompanied by two eagles, strikes down two figures, one of whom appears to symbolise Envy.

Similar in style to No.951.

DESIGNS FOR A COACH WITH THE CHIGI ARMS

953. 235 × 196 mm. Black chalk and black wash.   (4463)

954. 210 × 152 mm. Black chalk and black wash.   (5619)

No.953 shows the back of the coach with the arms supported by two allegorical figures; in No.954 the arms are enclosed in a circle and supported by putti.

The drawings may possibly be connected with a carnival chariot for Agostino Chigi (cf. Nos.50, 51).

955. **DESIGN FOR A RELIQUARY**   (5582)

213 × 92 mm. Pen and brown ink over red chalk.

DESIGNS FOR FRAMES

956. 242 × 115 mm. Pen and brown ink over black chalk. (*Fig. 100*)   (5643)

At the top a dragon, at the bottom a sphinx.

957. 277 × 122 mm. Pen and brown ink over black chalk.

At the top an eagle, at the bottom a lion.   (5580)

958. **DESIGN FOR A DECORATIVE PANEL**   (5579)

230 × 120 mm. Pen and brown ink over black chalk.

At the bottom a gryphon, at the top a fish-tailed figure.

959. DESIGN FOR A FINIAL   (5575)
174 × 132 mm. Pen and brown ink.

960. DESIGN FOR A CARTOUCHE   (5567)
257 × 177 mm. Pen and brown ink over black chalk.

DESIGNS FOR THE TOP OF A FRAME
961. 173 × 231 mm. Pen and brown ink over black chalk.
Squared. A scale at foot.   (4458)
With a coat of arms surmounted with a ducal coronet.

962. 315 × 187 mm. Pen and brown ink over black chalk.
                                           (5578)
Three designs, all including skulls, some crowned with laurel.
(*Fig. 101*)

963. AN EAGLE FLYING TOWARDS THE SUN   (5573)
159 × 140 mm. Pen and black ink, with grey wash.
These eight drawings are exactly in the manner of those
rough sketches attributed by Brauer and Wittkower to
G. P. Schor.

GIOVANNI PAOLO SCHOR
(attributed to)

964. DESIGN FOR THE ARMS OF ALEXANDER VII (4455)
245 × 122 mm. Pen and brown wash.

On the base, inscribed *AL. P.M.*, sit allegorical figures,
above whom is a structure having the Chigi arms on each
of its four faces and surmounted by putti carrying the keys
and the papal tiara.

GIOVANNI PAOLO SCHOR
(follower of)

965. DESIGN FOR A TABLE ORNAMENT   (4454)
257 × 154 mm. Pen and brown ink, with grey wash.

On a rock a seven-headed dragon supports a globe, on the
top of which sits a figure of the papacy. On either side of
the globe fly two figures carrying a Cross and a sceptre (?).
On the globe are the arms of Innocent XI (1676–89), and
the ornament may refer to his condemnation of Jansenism
in 1687.

DESIGNS FOR COACHES
966. 227 × 232 mm. Two drawings torn and stuck together.
Pen and brown ink, with grey wash.   (4464)

967. 227 × 215 mm. Two drawings torn and stuck together.
Pen and brown ink, with grey wash.   (5620)

968. 150 × 132 mm. Pen and brown wash over black chalk.
                                            (4465)

969. 220 × 85 mm. Pen and brown ink over black chalk.
                                            (5581)
All four drawings show the back of a coach. Nos.966 and
967 are decorated with eagles, No.968 with a sphere, and
No.969 with a crowned column.

These drawings, though like G. P. Schor in general conception, are quite different in execution from those usually
attributed to him, and were probably made by a member
of his studio.

970. DESIGN FOR A CHARIOT   (4480)
160 × 256 mm. Pen and brown wash.
A winged figure sits on a chariot seen from the side. Behind
her are an eagle and what may be a dragon.

971. DESIGN FOR A LOOKING-GLASS   (5574)
155 × 76 mm. Pen and bistre wash.
Foliage and putti, surmounted by a ducal coronet.

972. DESIGN FOR A CONSOLE TABLE   (4460)
135 × 220 mm. Pen and brown ink, with brown and grey
wash. A scale at the side.
The table is supported by two fish-tailed figures.

973. DESIGNS FOR MASKS   (5642)
122 × 252 mm. Two separate drawings torn and stuck together. Pen and brown wash.

974. DESIGN FOR AN ALTAR FRONTAL   (5556)
171 × 280 mm. Pen and pale brown wash. Inscribed: *3°B*
and *2°A*.
The design shows the Virgin and Child in Glory, adored by
angels. The arms have been identified by Dr. Arnold Noach
as those of Max Gandolf Kuenburg, who was Archbishop
of Salzburg from 1668 to 1687.

DESIGNS FOR A FOUNTAIN
975. 304 × 212 mm. Pen and brown ink, with grey wash.
With a scale.   (4470)

976. 307 × 213 mm. Pen and brown ink, with grey wash.
With a scale.   (4468)

977. 307 × 212 mm. Pen and brown ink, with grey wash.
With a scale.   (4467)
These three drawings are certainly by the same hand and
probably variant designs for the same fountain. In technique
they are close to Schor, but they are more rigidly architectural than most of his designs. They are probably by a
member of his studio with some specialist training in
architecture.

978. DESIGN FOR A CANOPY   (5572)
242 × 190 mm. Pen and brown ink, with grey-brown wash.
Inscribed: *parte del . . . di rame indorato che . . . della . . . Carozza.*
From the inscription, presumably a design for the upper
part of a coach.

PIETRO TESTA
(1607 or 1611–50)

Except for No.987, which was loose, the following
drawings form a series attributed to Testa in Inventory

A (p. 127). One, No.982, is for a known engraving by him, and one (No.983) has attached to it a letter in his hand. Eleven (Nos.988–998) are copies after other engravings. Of the remainder some, such as Nos.979, 980, 986, and 999, are characteristic of his usual style of figure drawing. One, a red chalk academy (No.987), has an old inscription, but there are no other drawings of similar subjects on which to base a stylistic comparison. Two, Nos.984 and 985, are less like his known work, and the former is near the difficult borderline between Testa and Mola. In view of the old attribution however, it has been left with the Testas.

A much more difficult problem is that of possible drawings by Testa after the Antique at Windsor. Baldinucci states (*Notizie dei Professori del Disegno*, 1845–7, v, p. 313) that Testa made 'di sua mano' five volumes of such drawings for Cassiano dal Pozzo. These were divided as follows:

1. 'tutte quelle cose . . . che alla falsa opinione appartengono, tanto di deità quanto di sacrificii'.

2. 'Riti nuziali, abiti consolari, e di matrone, inscrizioni, abiti di artefici, materie lugubri, spettacoli, cose rusticali, bagni e triclini'.

3. 'I bassirilievi, che si vedono negli archi trionfali, storie romane e favole'.

4. 'Vasi, statue, utensili diversi antichi'.

5. 'Le figure del Vergilio antico e del Terenzio della Vaticana, il musaico del tempio della Fortuna di Preneste, oggi Palestrina, fatto da Silla, ed altre cose colorite'.

Since most of Cassiano dal Pozzo's collection came, via the Albani, to Windsor, it is logical to look for these volumes here, but the problem is not easy. There are copies of the Palestrina mosaic and the Vatican Terence and Virgil, but these copies bear no resemblance to the style of Testa. The bulk of the volumes belonging to Cassiano dal Pozzo were rebound in the time of George III and their contents apparently mixed with other material to form new volumes. It is not, therefore, possible to find any volumes corresponding to those described by Baldinucci, except in one case. One volume (numbered 184) survives in what seems to be its original form. It contains 109 drawings (Nos.10189–10297), and on the first page is the red seal identified by Ashby as belonging to a member of the Pozzo family. The contents correspond to those of Baldinucci's fourth volume, and the drawings, with the possible exception of No.10297, seem to be all by one hand. They are not, however, at all like Testa's known work. On the other hand his drawings for Cassiano were probably made when he first came to Rome, since they were mere hack-work, and we have little evidence of Testa's early manner. It is therefore possible, though not likely, that these drawings are in fact by him. If this is so, there are many others scattered through the volumes of drawings after the Antique which seem to be by the same hand, and which no doubt formed part of the other volumes. In particular one group may be mentioned illustrating ancient feasts, including several representations of the Triclinium (Nos. 8418–8439), which may well form part of Baldinucci's second volume. All these drawings are in a technique based on that of Cortona, in whose studio Testa worked for some time after his first master, Domenichino, left for Naples in 1629. The attribution of these drawings must, however, remain uncertain, and as their principal interest is as records of works of ancient art, they have been omitted from the present volume and will, it is hoped, be published in a forthcoming work by Mr. Cornelius Vermeule, who has already prepared a typescript catalogue of the whole series of Pozzo's drawings after the Antique at Windsor.

979. THE DRUNKENNESS OF NOAH (*Fig. 102*)   (5938)
239 × 175 mm. Pen and brown ink.

980. A BEARDED SAINT BORNE UP BY ANGELS AND PUTTI
186 × 222 mm. Pen and brown wash.   (5933)
Another drawing for the same group, but in a lunette and with other figures, is in the Louvre (1885; cf. A. Marabottini, *Commentari*, v, 1954, p. 243, and Pl. lxvi, Fig. 10).

Fig. 102   Cat. No. 979

Fig. 103   Cat. No. 982

981. 'DEPOSUIT POTENTES'   (5939)

389 × 279 mm. Pen and brown ink, black and white chalk, on blue paper. On the cartellino the inscription: *Deposuit potentes de sede et exaltabit humiles.*

At the top God the Father, seated, makes a gesture of command. Below to the right two figures, one of whom holds a cartellino with the inscription, and the other holds a snake (Wisdom). Below them is the throne, before which kneels the humble man, while the King lies in the left foreground biting his hand in despair. The drawing looks as though it was designed for an engraving, but none is known.

982. BACCHANAL (*Fig. 103*)   (5937)

234 × 197 mm. Pen and brown ink over red chalk, on discoloured white paper.

Study for three dancing figures in the engraving of *Autumn or the Indian Triumph of Bacchus* (B. 38; cf. No.996). Another drawing for the engraving is at Frankfurt.

983. THE FEAST OF MIDAS (*Fig. 104*)   (5932)

270 × 209 mm. Pen and brown ink. Inscribed: *quel Mida che tanto nè tiraneggia.*

An engraving, either executed or published by Vincenzo Billij in Rome, probably in the early eighteenth century, represents this design. It lacks many details of the drawing, but, given the generally schematic nature of Billij's engravings after Testa, it is probably a crude version of this drawing rather than an accurate engraving after a less finished sketch.

Attached to the drawing is a two-page letter in Testa's hand, which reads as follows:

Sig. mio sempre . . .

E' troppo alta l'injuria in paragone della destrezza che pure è infinita, che VS. à usato per cavarmelo, e io che non sono mal' Mattematico, haveva da' fatti Vostri previsto ogni male, in sòma è troppo dificile fabricare unal salda Amicizia, e mostrar la vivezza de' gli affetti; dico dificile per che questo maledetto oro per tutto vuol' dar di naso, e che frutti dunque partorira pianta tanto nobbile, è rara della Amicitia? se' però io troppo non presumo, non mi vanto; De' caro Sre Simonelli lasciamo questa maledetta forza del oro alla tirània de' grandi; dico questo ora per tutto cio che trà noi potrà succedere, ò pure Lei in costesto modo sigilla, è non vuol più comandarmi? io in soma non posso credere che VS. di me pensa tal' bassezza ma la furia di questo turbidissimo torrente di tanti Midi alla moda l'ha fatto scorrere, errore per mia fe', che per mai, mai, mai dal Sre Simonelli aspettava; io pensavo, da queste mie prime poche bagatelle, havere alsato, da i fondamenti d'una perfetta benevolezza, un poco d'una (per così dire tal parete, da potermi in tempi più affanosi salvarmi e godere le dolcezze d'una pretiosissima e dà mè sempre desiderata Amicitia, è VS. così non so perche, mi pare non questi mi voglia mandare à terra il poco, forse parendovi io troppo temerario, è che m'impediate il di nuovo comincare col accennarmi che (non che altro) io posso non scrivervi per non caricarvi (dite Voi) di tanti hobligi, se questo c'havete in testa e in verità lo scrivete, che pure tanto male per hora non voglio persuadermi Voi, in buona gratia nostra, pizichate un tant . . . del Tiranno, quì nonche potendo per per seguitare in infinite doglierse, pregandovi à diperiare cotesto gigantissimo erroracco col' adoperarmi sempre in quel' pochissimo niente ch'io vaglio sempre semprissime è di quella Libbertà che dovete, che troppo mi sotisfa il gusto che servendo che di tanto merita, io sento è di tanto io havro e pensandomi fermissimamente che il medio che il farete, e che del' fatto cordialissimamente vi pentiate, senza fine, io, io, ma io vi adoro senza loro.

A Sr. Abati centomillanta raccomandationi. Roma dì 22 Ag.to 165 . . .

Io sò che questo chiasso bravatorio Voi l'aspettai, perche havete cervello, è sapete che li Amici non siano trattati così, imparate à buttar le debole. con questa collera mi si era scordato ringratiarvi de i guanti i quali stano benissime; diferi che non da qui non ho campo. è delle tragedie Romane che in pane? gran Roma è questa teatro sempre di cosonè, coselle, cosacce.

Sre et Amico . . . mo.

Fig. 104   Cat. No. 983

in tanto anderò osservando le meraviglie della natura che adopri tanto artifizio, e diligenza intorno à cosa che pure mai vede lume potendoli bastare in semplice schizo, o pure à previsto questo nostra curiosità? et che voi per essa, vogliate significarmi. S'io rinvengo tanto scapperò per le piazze furiosamente vantandome, e di costa ne sentirete i gridi.

Pietro Testa

Ridurrei questa favola antica al uso moderno così; che non che alle Virtù, quello anchè che va per nutrimento la convertono in oro per empire i sacchi che vi pare di questi miei fantasmi e chinibizzi (?) sono argomenti di satirette assai bizarre che se il Tempo mel' concedesse chi sà che un d' anch'io col mattitatoio non vada in Parnaso. vedete che carta che coglinerie vi scrivo.

Simonelli, to whom the letter is addressed, was a patron of Testa's. We may conclude from the not very clear argument of the letter that the artist was in financial difficulties, apparently over a debt, and makes this the opportunity for a disquisition on the evil effects of riches, as symbolized in the story of Midas.

The editors wish to thank Mr. Francis Haskell for help in reading and interpreting this text.

Fig. 105   Cat. No. 984

984. HERCULES AND ANTAEUS (*Fig. 105*)   (5936)
247 × 155 mm. Pen and brown ink.

985. POLYPHEMUS HURLING A ROCK AT ULYSSES
(5934)
201 × 106 mm. Pen and brown ink. Inscribed at the bottom: *l'allecato Polifemo che getta lo smisurato scoglio dietro alla nave del fugitivo Ulisse.*

986. STANDING FIGURE OF A WOMAN WITH ONE ARM RAISED   (5935)
192 × 110 mm. Pen and brown wash over black chalk.
More finished than the preceding drawings, and perhaps a study for a figure in a big composition which has not hitherto been identified.

PIETRO TESTA
(attributed to)

987. A KNEELING NUDE MODEL   (5931)
376 × 247 mm. Red chalk. Inscribed: *Pietro Testa.*
This is unlike any known drawings by Testa, but the inscription appears to date from the early eighteenth century.

PIETRO TESTA
(after)

ALLEGORY OF VIRTUE AND KNOWLEDGE
988. 381 × 277 mm. Pen and brown ink, with black wash.
(5942)
989. 377 × 262 mm. Pen and brown ink, with black wash.
(5945)
These two drawings make up the composition of Bartsch, 32.

THE TRIUMPH OF PAINTING
990. 447 × 360 mm. Pen and brown ink, with black wash.
(5947)
991. 427 × 353 mm. Pen and brown ink, with black wash.
(5948)
These two drawings make up the composition of Bartsch, 35.

SPRING
992. 469 × 348 mm. Pen and brown ink, with black wash.
(5950)
993. 475 × 346 mm. Pen and brown ink, with black wash.
(5944)
These drawings together make up Bartsch, 36.

SUMMER
994. 472 × 351 mm. Pen and brown ink, with black wash.
(5949)
995. 483 × 336 mm. Pen and brown ink, with black wash.
(5946)
These two drawings together make up Bartsch, 37.

996. AUTUMN
488 × 348 mm. Pen and brown ink, with black wash, partly ruled in brown ink.   (5940)
This drawing is identical with the left half of Bartsch, 38.

WINTER

997. 483 × 342 mm. Pen and brown ink, with black wash. (5943)

998. 482 × 342 mm. Pen and brown ink, with black wash. (5941)

The above eleven drawings are fairly exact copies after engravings by Testa.

999. WAR DRIVING OUT THE ARTS OF PEACE (5951)
333 × 453 mm. Pen and brown ink, over black chalk.
In the centre Mars in his chariot advances towards the right. At the sight of him Justice and Peace fly away up to Heaven, Painting faints away, while another allegorical figure attempts to stop the horses. The chariot is accompanied by figures of Violence and Discord.
A feeble drawing, probably a copy of an original by Testa.

FRANCESCO TREVISANI (1656—1746)
(attributed to)

1000. THE HOLY FAMILY (*Plate 65*) (5329)
265 × 373 mm. Black and white chalk on buff paper.

1001. THE HOLY FAMILY (3810)
363 × 467 mm. Black and white chalk on buff paper.
From the volumes of *Bolognesi Moderni*.

The attribution of these two drawings is based on the similarity of types and composition to a painting by Trevisani at Dresden (No.447).

1002. DANIEL IN THE LION'S DEN (3753)
497 × 347 mm. Black and white chalk on buff paper.
From the volumes of *Bolognesi Moderni*.

Similar in style and technique to the first two drawings.

CLELIA VALERI
(active 1828)

Three careful miniature copies of pictures, in water-colour, body-colour and gum, have been inserted by Sir William Drummond in his presentation volumes of the *Odes of Horace* given to King George IV in 1828.

Vol. I. Frontispiece. After Lawrence: King George IV.

    262 × 186 mm. Within gold border, water-colour, body-colour, gum. Inscribed on the mount: *Copied by Clelia Valerj Rome 1828*. An inscription on the verso of the leaf states that it is copied *from the Original picture in the Vatican presented by His Majesty to Pope Pius VII*.

Vol. II. Frontispiece. Pope Leo XII.

    97 × 85 mm. Within gold border, water-colour, body-colour, gum. Inscribed (probably by C. Ruspi, q.v.): *Fatto da Clelia Valerj Roma 1828*.

    Second frontispiece. Cardinal della Somaglia.

    96 × 87 mm. Similar to the preceding; similarly inscribed.

See under Sir William Gell in the *Catalogue of English Drawings*.

FRANCESCO VILLAMENA (1566–1626)
(attributed to)

1003. PORTRAIT OF A MAN WITH HIS HAT IN HIS HAND
142 × 118 mm. Black and red chalk. (0254)
The traditional attribution to Villamena seems convincing.

FRANCESCO VILLAMENA
(after)

COPIES OF 'LES GOURMEURS'
A painting formerly in the Lucien Bonaparte collection (reproduced in *L'Arte*, xxxviii, 1935, p. 206).

1004. THREE FIGURES (5316)
255 × 316 mm. Red chalk.

1005. A MAN WITH A DOG (2340)
263 × 130 mm. Irregularly cut. Black and red chalk.

ANONYMOUS DRAWINGS

1006. STUDY FOR THE HEAD OF ST. JEROME (*Plate 2*)
368 × 235 mm. Red chalk. (4873)

1007. PORTRAIT OF DONNA OLIMPIA MUTI CAFFARELLI
    (*Plate 3*) (6350)
392 × 250 mm. Red chalk. Inscribed: *Olimpia Muti Caffarelli obiit Anno 1643 etatis sue 80 Marchesa di Turano Camarda e fileti.*

These two drawings must be by the same hand, although the first comes from the Sacchi volumes and the second from the Elisabetta Sirani series. Sirani was only born five years before the death of the sitter and is, therefore, automatically excluded. In technique both drawings have something in common with Sacchi's manner, but he would never have risked anything so bold as the arrangement of nose, eyebrow and eye-lashes in the St. Jerome. The style of draughtsmanship also suggests Guido Reni, but since he left Rome in 1622, he is unlikely to have had the opportunity of painting the Roman lady at the age at which she appears.
The *St. Jerome* is strikingly like in type to the head in a painting in a private collection in Milan attributed by Professor Longhi to Orazio Gentileschi (repr. *Proporzioni*, i, 1943, Pl. 40). On the other hand, Gentileschi left Rome in 1621, so the same objection can be made to this attribution as in the case of Reni. At present, therefore, it seems safest to ascribe these two impressive drawings to an unknown Roman artist working in the 1630's, the date being suggested by the apparent age of the sitter in No.1007.

1008. THE ASCENSION (4536)
85 × 235 mm. Pen, with black ink, and grey wash.

1009. ST. PETER ENTHRONED (4535)
107 × 226 mm. Pen, with black ink and grey wash.

1010. DESIGN FOR A MONUMENT (5608)
186 × 107 mm. Pen, with black ink and grey wash, over black chalk. Inscribed: *Bernino*.

1011. DESIGN FOR A TABLE FOUNTAIN (4471)
243×171 mm. Pen, with black ink and grey wash, over black chalk.

1012. DESIGN FOR A VASE (5629)
386×266 mm. Pen and brown ink, with grey wash, over black chalk. Inscribed: *Bernino.*
The vase is decorated with a procession of Silenus.

DESIGNS FOR AN EWER
1013. 370×238 mm. Pen and brown ink, with grey wash, over black chalk. Inscribed: *Bernino.* (5630)
Decorated with the story of Polyphemus, Acis and Galatea.

1014. 394×255 mm. Pen and brown ink, with grey wash. Inscribed: *Bernino.* (5631)

DESIGNS FOR A HANGING LAMP
1015. 232×268 mm. Pen and brown ink, with grey wash. (5632)

1016. 231×270 mm. Pen and brown ink, with grey wash. (5633)
Each is decorated with a scene from the Passion.

These nine drawings are from the Bernini volumes, except for Nos.1008, 1009, 1011, which are from the Cortona volumes. They are apparently all by the same hand and seem to date from the very end of the seventeenth century. They are probably by a sculptor who was primarily working in silver. Nos.1011–1016 seem to be designs for small silver objects; Nos.1008, 1009, could well be for silver plaques, and No.1010 alone seems to be for a larger commemorative sculpture, perhaps a tomb.

1017. JAEL AND SISERA (5055)
209×271 mm. Pen and brown wash over black chalk.

1018. THE VISITATION (01198)
490×380 mm. Red chalk, pen and brown wash, heightened with body-colour, on brown-toned paper.
Probably by a late follower of Pietro da Cortona.

1019. THE HOLY FAMILY (0199)
244×178 mm. Red chalk. The old mount had an ascription to Camassei.

1020. THE FLIGHT INTO EGYPT (0198)
255×185 mm. Red chalk. The old mount had an ascription to Camassei.

1021. CHRIST CALMING THE STORM (4527)
Circular. 207 mm. in diameter. Black and white chalk on grey paper.

1022. STUDY FOR THE DEAD CHRIST (4344)
362×402 mm. Black and white chalk on blue paper.
The old mount had an ascription to P. F. Mola.

1023. THE CORONATION OF THE VIRGIN (4418)
Circular. 290 mm. in diameter. Pen and brown wash, heightened with white.
From the Maratta volumes.
By a contemporary of Maratta, but not by his own hand.

1024. THE EXECUTION OF A MARTYR (1327)
427×320 mm. Red and black chalk with pen and brown ink.
From the Domenichino volumes, but by an artist who also knew the work of Pietro da Cortona.

1025. THE VIRGIN AND CHILD ADORED BY A BISHOP AND A PRIEST (6804)
426×282 mm. Red chalk, pen and grey-brown wash.

1026. ST. AGATHA IN GLORY (*Fig. 106*) (6818)
305×196 mm. Pen and brown wash, in feigned oval.

1027. THE VISION OF A HERMIT (*Fig. 107*) (6805)
310×217 mm. Red chalk, pen and brown wash.

1028. FAITH ADORED BY A GROUP OF MONKS (0259)
Circular. 191 mm. in diameter. Red chalk.
The old mount had an ascription to Pietro Locatelli.

1029. ST. JOHN (5672)
226×172 mm. Red chalk, with touches of pen and brown ink on grey paper, in a feigned oval.
From the Lanfranco volumes.

1030. ST. SEBASTIAN (4583)
297×156 mm. Red chalk.
From the Stefano della Bella volume.

1030a. CLEMENT VIII IN BOLOGNA (5983)
119×184 mm. Pen and brown ink, with light brown washes.
The drawing shows a kneeling ecclesiastic presenting a book to the Pope. In the background are the leaning towers of Bologna. The arms on the throne are those of the Aldobrandini family, and the scene represented must therefore be the visit of Clement VIII to Bologna in 1598, after receiving the submission of Ferrara.

1031. ALLEGORY OF THE PAPACY (6750)
282×215 mm. Red chalk, touches of white, on grey paper.
A figure, apparently a woman, on clouds, holding the keys.

1032. THE VIRGIN AND CHILD APPEARING TO A MONK (*Fig. 108*) (5954)
262×181 mm. Pen and brown wash, heightened with body-colour, on brown paper.

1033. A MONK CARRIED UP TO HEAVEN (6718)
170×309 mm. Pen and brown wash, heightened with body-colour, on grey-brown paper. Squared. The composition shaped to a quatrefoil. Inscribed: *Ludovico Gemignani.*
Possibly connected with the decoration of S. Andrea al Quirinale (cf. below, No.1044).

Fig. 106   Cat. No. 1026   Fig. 107   Cat. No. 1027   Fig. 108   Cat. No. 1032

Fig. 109   Cat. No. 1035   Fig. 110   Cat. No. 1039   Fig. 111   Cat. No. 1040

1034. A BEARDED SAINT IN ADORATION   (0176)

242 × 179 mm. Pen and brown wash.

The old mount had an ascription to Giacomo Cortese.

1035. THE RISEN CHRIST APPEARING TO A MONK (6742)
                                             (*Fig. 109*)

342 × 340 mm. Pen and brown ink, with grey wash, heightened with body-colour, now discoloured. Squared.

A late seventeenth-century drawing.

1036. A MONK KNEELING BEFORE AN ALTAR, WITH PRIESTS BEHIND AND ANGELS ABOVE   (6749)

238 × 156 mm. Red chalk.

From the first half of the century.

1037. SIX SAINTS IN CLOUDS   (6751)

172 × 325 mm. Pen and brown ink, with grey wash, heightened with white, over black chalk, on blue-grey paper.

The Saints include three bishops and a nun.

1038. A GROUP OF SAINTS IN GLORY   (6737)

300 × 215 mm. Pen and black wash, heightened with body-colour. In a feigned oval. Inscribed with a name which might be *Turroni*, or *Terroni*, or *Furroni*, or *Ferroni*.

Two of the Saints appear to be Benedictines, and one is a soldier in armour carrying a banner.

1039. A GIRL TAKING A VOW OF POVERTY (*Fig. 110*)
                                             (5654)

209 × 142 mm. Pen and brown wash, heightened with body-colour, over black chalk.

Inv. A, p. 110: From a volume containing works by Pietro de Pietri and other pupils of Maratta.

Probably about 1700.

1040. TWO HERMITS (*Fig. 111*)   (1776)

260 × 196 mm. Pen and brown and red wash, on darkened grey paper. Inscribed on mount: *Caracci*.

1041. THE VISION OF A SAINT   (4145)

206 × 286 mm. Pen and brown wash, heightened with body-colour, on brown paper.

1042. ALLEGORY OF INNOCENCE   (6791)

182 × 234 mm. Pen and brown wash over black chalk.

A woman stands on the head of a dragon, while lambs play around her.

1043. AN ALLEGORICAL FIGURE   (6813)

264 × 187 mm. The composition is oval. Black chalk. Squared.

1044. ANGELS ROUND A SARCOPHAGUS PLAYING MUSI-CAL INSTRUMENTS   (4420)

160 × 253 mm. The composition enclosed in a quatrefoil. Pen and brown ink, with yellow wash and touches of body-colour.

A drawing for the same composition, in the same shaped panel, is in the Albertina (*Zeichnungen der toskanischen, umbrischen und römischen Schulen*, No.797), where it is wrongly ascribed to Passeri. Another drawing at Düsseldorf (No.466), showing a *Saint in Glory*, has exactly the same complex quatrefoil shape for the main panel and is a study by Odazzi for the ceiling fresco of *S. Luigi Gonzaga in Glory* in one of the side chapels of S. Andrea al Quirinale. It is possible, there-fore, that No.1044 may be connected with the decoration of the same church. The same may be true of No.1033, which is in general design like the Düsseldorf drawing.

1045. AN ANGEL CROWNING A YOUTH AND A GIRL   (5517)

183 × 183 mm. Pen and black ink, with grey-brown wash.

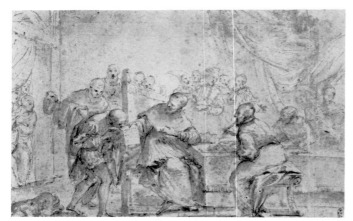

Fig. 112   Cat. No. 1046

Fig. 113   Cat. No. 1052

Fig. 114   Cat. No. 1049

Fig. 115   Cat. No. 1053

Fig. 116   Cat. No. 1060

Fig. 117   Cat. No. 1047

1046. A POPE HANDING A PAPER TO A SUPPLIANT
(Fig. 112)   (0363)

190 × 296 mm. Pen and brown wash. The old mount had an ascription to D. M. Canuti.

Probably from the first quarter of the seventeenth century.

1047. A COUNCIL FOR THE REUNION OF THE EASTERN AND WESTERN CHURCHES *(Fig. 117)*   (6713)

235 × 373 mm. Pen and brown wash over black chalk, heightened with body-colour. Inscribed: *Lodovico Gemignani*.

In the background a pope enthroned presides over an assembly consisting half of Catholic bishops and half of Orthodox patriarchs. On either side of the pope stand two figures, who appear to be Eastern and Western Emperors, and to this group there appears on a cloud a bearded Saint, probably St. Peter. On the extreme left a Catholic bishop reads to the assembly from a pulpit. The drawing seems to represent a council discussing the reunion of the Eastern and Western Churches.

The style does not confirm the old attribution to Lodovico Gimignani.

1048. INNOCENT XII SURROUNDED BY ALLEGORICAL FIGURES   (6717)

321 × 221 mm. Red and black chalk. Inscribed: *Lodovico Gemignani*.

Among the allegorical figures Faith, Religion, and Charity are distinguishable. In the background are various buildings,

including St. Peter's and Monte Citorio. As Innocent only acquired the latter in 1697, the drawing is unlikely to be by Lodovico Gimignani, who died in that year. In any case the style is not like his. Probably for the frontispiece of a book.

1049. AN ALLEGORY OF THE ARTS *(Fig. 114)*   (6811)

429 × 349 mm. Black and red chalk, brown and grey wash, heightened with white, on buff paper. Inscribed: *Luigi Garzi*.

Unlike Garzi's usually very distinguishable style.

1050. AN ALLEGORY OF DAWN   (4489)

392 × 260 mm. In a quatrefoil. Pen and brown wash, heightened with body-colour, over black chalk, on blue paper.

Inscribed: *NOCTEMQUE VIGIL . . . DUCEBAT; berretini*, and in the 'deceptive' hand: *Cortona*.

Exh.: 17th Century Art, Royal Academy, London, 1938, No. 432, as Maratta.

Aurora in a chariot drawn by lions, accompanied by Hercules, drives away Night.

Not by either Cortona or Maratta.

1051. APOLLO AND MINERVA ON PARNASSUS   (8322)

255 × 490 mm. Black chalk.

On the right Apollo, accompanied by Pegasus and the Muses, gives a bowl to a kneeling poet, who is crowned by a Muse. To the left Minerva helps two aspirants to reach

Fig. 118　　　　　　　　　　　　Cat. No. 1063

A Roman priest stands beside an altar, about to pour a libation. A soldier and other figures kneel before the altar, and above Fame and a putto carry a coat of arms surmounted by a coronet (? ducal). A radiant sun appears on the altar and elsewhere in the design, and bees appear at several points. The bees and the sun, which are much used as a decorative motive on the Palazzo Barberini, indicate a connection with that family. This connection is confirmed by the style of the drawing, which suggests a classical member of the Barberini group, familiar with the early work of Cortona. Probably the same hand as No.1060, and possibly a design for the title-page of a book.

1054. ROMULUS AND REMUS　　　　　　　　(3606)

165 × 208 mm. Black chalk. Drawn in an oval. Inscribed: *Baciccia*.

A weak drawing of about the middle of the century, and in no way connected with Gaulli.

1055. A SATYR TIED TO A TREE AND MOCKED BY A WOMAN　　　　　　　　　　　　　　　　(6792)

168 × 240 mm. Pen and brown wash over black chalk.

A winged putto points out the satyr in scorn to a goat-footed putto. No doubt an allegory of sensuality. Probably dates from the middle of the century.

1056. CHARITY　　　　　　　　　　　　　　(6755)

172 × 136 mm. Pen and brown ink, with grey-brown wash, heightened with body-colour, on a prepared surface.

Probably for a painted decoration over a pediment, dating from about 1700.

1057. HOPE, CHARITY, CONSTANCY, AND FORTITUDE　　　　　　　　　　　　　　　　　(5555)

223 × 274 mm. Pen and brown ink, with brown and grey wash. Inscribed: *Bernino*.

Probably eighteenth century.

TWO SATYR BOYS

1058. 400 × 241 mm. Black chalk, with touches of white, on grey paper.　　　　　　　　　　　　　　　(5310)

1059. 400 × 252 mm. Black chalk, with touches of white, on grey paper.　　　　　　　　　　　　　　　(5311)

A variation on the decorative figures at the ends of the ceiling of the Farnese Gallery.

1060. THE VICTORY OF GODFREY DE BOUILLON (0118)

409 × 200 mm. A strip added at the top. Pen and brown ink. with brown and grey wash. Torn and mended. (*Fig. 116*)

Outside the walls of Jerusalem three kings kneel in surrender to a knight, who is crowned by Fame. Probably by the same hand as No.1053, and perhaps also for an engraving. A study for this, showing the knight and the figure of Fame only, was sold in the Loyd sale (Sotheby's, 28.xi.1945, lot 46) with an eighteenth-century attribution to Salvator Rosa.

1061. A TRAVELLER IN CONVERSATION WITH A WOMAN　　　　　　　　　　　　　　　　　　(4157)

182 × 205 mm. Originally circular, but cut on all four sides.

the top of the mountain. In the left background Silenus on his donkey. Perhaps a drawing for an engraving. A similar theme was treated by Lazzaro Baldi in two paintings in the Spada Gallery (cf. F. Zeri, *La Galleria Spada in Rome*, Florence, 1954, pp. 26 f., Nos.17, 23).

A group of drawings after the Antique, apparently by the same hand, is in the Pozzo volumes (Inv. No.8261ff.).

1052. DIANA AND ENDYMION (*Fig. 113*)　　(4156)

281 × 401 mm. Pen and brown wash over black chalk.

From the Maratta volumes.

The chariot of Apollo drives away Night. In the foreground Diana stands beside Endymion, whom two putti cover with a sheet.

Probably dates from the middle of the seventeenth century.

1053. A SACRIFICE (*Fig. 115*)　　　　　　(4486)

309 × 201 mm. Pen and bistre wash. Much rubbed, and retouched in one area with grey wash. Pressed through with a stylus.

Inv. A, p. 113: From a volume containing drawings by Cortona.

Pen and brown wash, heightened with white, on brown paper.

From the Maratta volumes.

The woman is seated on a plinth between columns, with treasure piled up in front of her. The pyramid and the palm tree in the background suggest that the subject is connected with Egypt, but it has so far not been identified. The drawing seems to date from the end of the seventeenth century.

1062. FIGURES BY THE SEA-SHORE   (6120)

151 × 155 mm. Grey-brown wash.

Verso: Drawing of ancient monuments, including a pyramid.

Inv. A, p. 113, as Salvator Rosa.

The *recto* is connected with paintings ascribed to Salvator Rosa, but both *recto* and *verso* drawings clearly date from the mid-eighteenth century.

1063. A GROUP OF FIGURES ROUND AN OIL-LAMP

202 × 135 mm. Pen and brown wash. *(Fig. 118)*   (5520)

A drawing by an artist interested in strong light effects. Probably by a post-Caravaggesque, but just possibly by one of his late sixteenth-century predecessors.

1064. A BEARDED MAN IN ADORATION   (4961)

177 × 157 mm. Red and black chalk, with touches of white, on grey paper.

From the Sacchi volumes, but clearly eighteenth-century.

Probably a study for an *Adoration of the Shepherds.*

1065. STUDY OF A PARTLY DRAPED FIGURE   (883)

193 × 250 mm. Black and white chalk on grey-blue paper.

Verso: A seated nude. Brown wash, heightened with body-colour, over black chalk.

From the Domenichino volumes.

Probably dating from the first quarter of the seventeenth century.

1066. A WOMAN AND A CHILD   (4369)

363 × 240 mm. Black and white chalk on rough buff paper.

From the Maratta volumes.

Probably by an artist of the first half of the seventeenth century.

1067. A FIGURE SEATED ON A CLOUD   (2063)

289 × 227 mm. Black and white chalk on grey-blue paper.

From the Carracci volumes.

Probably by one of their Roman followers.

1068. A MALE NUDE HOLDING A TABLET AND A CANDLE

240 × 292 mm. Red chalk.   (5712)

From the Lanfranco volumes.

Probably by a Roman contemporary of Lanfranco. A drawing, identical in everything except the head, is among the anonymous Italian drawings from the Fenwick collection in the British Museum (1946–7–13–1304).

Fig. 119   Cat. No. 1073

1069. A MALE NUDE SEATED ON A ROCK   (4908)

407 × 230 mm. Red chalk, heightened with body-colour.

From the Sacchi volumes.

1070. A MALE NUDE SEATED ON A ROCK, SEEN FROM BEHIND   (4912)

414 × 276 mm. Dark red chalk, heightened with white (oxydised).

From the Sacchi volumes.

Probably by a sculptor familiar with the work of Bernini, and working at the very end of the seventeenth century.

1071. A PARTLY DRAPED MALE FIGURE   (13038)

170 × 215 mm. Red chalk, left-hand shading.

Somewhat in the manner of Sacchi.

1072. A FORESHORTENED MALE NUDE   (5536)

404 × 536 mm. Black chalk. Inscribed: *Cav.^e Bernini.*

A feeble drawing, imitating the manner of Bernini.

1073. PORTRAIT OF A MAN WEARING A WIG   (5188)

296 × 211 mm. Red chalk. *(Fig. 119)*

A drawing like Maratta in technique, but of a naturalism unusual in Roman art of the late seventeenth century.

1074. HEAD OF A GIRL   (354)

255 × 178 mm. Red chalk. In a drawn octagon.

From the Domenichino volumes.

By an artist of the second half of the seventeenth century.

1075. HEAD OF A GIRL   (513)

156 × 106 mm. Black chalk on grey paper.

From the Domenichino volumes.

Reminiscent of the manner of Sacchi or the early Maratta.

1076. HEADS OF A WOMAN AND A CHILD   (5405)

272 × 202 mm. Red chalk.

The drawing is laid down, but an inscription on the back can be partially deciphered, including a date which appears to read 1618, though the last figure is doubtful.

1077. HEAD OF A CHILD   (4874)

265 × 300 mm. Black chalk, with touches of white, on blue paper.

From the Sacchi volumes.

Too feeble to be by Sacchi, but probably by a Roman contemporary.

1078. CLASSICAL MASK, PERHAPS OF JUPITER (5361)

379 × 282 mm. Black chalk, with touches of white, on grey paper.

1079. MASK OF A SATYR   (0299)

243 × 202 mm. Black chalk on grey paper.

1080. HEAD OF A YOUTH   (2029)

255 × 192 mm. Black chalk.

1081. VIEW OF BRACCIANO   (5816)

96 × 194 mm. Black chalk on pink prepared paper.

1082. ROUGH SKETCH OF A SATYR   (5526)

141 × 117 mm. Pen and brown ink. Inscribed with capital letters forming two not clearly decipherable monograms.

A drawing of the first half of the seventeenth century.

1083. LANDSCAPE WITH A MAN DRIVING A DONKEY
                                         (5755)

227 × 178 mm. Black chalk, touched with pen and brown ink.

1084. DESIGN FOR A FRAME FOR A PORTRAIT (4422)

259 × 185 mm. Black chalk.

Inv. A, p. 110: From a volume including Pietro de Pietri, Masucci and other followers of Maratta.

Two putti hold a wreath at the top of an oval space, evidently intended for a portrait. Below a bundle of brushes and a maulstick. Probably for an engraving.

Probably c.1700.

1085. DESIGN FOR THE COAT OF ARMS OF AN ECCLESI-ASTIC (*Fig. 120*)   (6765)

211 × 282 mm. Pen and brown wash, on slight red chalk.

Four allegorical figures, two of whom support the shield, are accompanied by putti, who hold back a canopy. To the right a gryphon, apparently as a supporter.

Probably dating from the first quarter of the seventeenth century.

Fig. 120   Cat. No. 1085

PLATES

I. ATTRIBUTED TO ANGELO CAROSELLI: JUDITH AND HOLOFERNES (Cat. No. 106)

2. ROMAN SCHOOL: STUDY FOR THE HEAD OF ST. JEROME (Cat. No. 1006)

Olimpia Muti Caffarelli Obiit Anno 1643 etatis sue 80
marchesa di Sorano seconda e felici

3. ROMAN SCHOOL: PORTRAIT OF DONNA OLIMPIA MUTI CAFFARELLI (Cat. No. 1007)

4. GIOVANNI LANFRANCO: STUDY FOR AN *IGNUDO* (Cat. No. 216)

5. GIOVANNI LANFRANCO: STUDY OF A WOMAN (Cat. No. 211)

6. GIOVANNI LANFRANCO: STUDY FOR ST. THOMAS (Cat. No. 199)

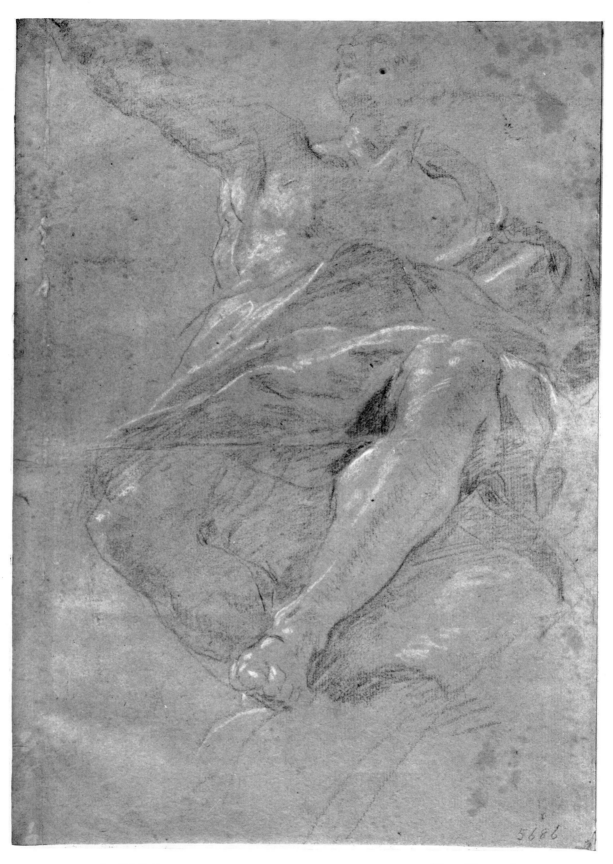

7. GIOVANNI LANFRANCO: STUDY FOR A PROPHET (Cat. No. 197)

8. GIOVANNI LORENZO BERNINI: PORTRAIT OF A BOY (Cat. No. 55)

9. GIOVANNI LORENZO BERNINI: SELF-PORTRAIT (Cat. No. 54)

10–11. GIOVANNI LORENZO BERNINI: STUDIES FOR THE FONTANA DEL MORO (Cat. Nos. 41 and 40)

12. GIOVANNI LORENZO BERNINI: DESIGN FOR A FOUNTAIN OF NEPTUNE (Cat. No. 42)

13. GIOVANNI LORENZO BERNINI: STUDY FOR A FOUNTAIN OF NEPTUNE (Cat. No. 44)

14. GIOVANNI LORENZO BERNINI: STUDY FOR A FOUNTAIN OF NEPTUNE (Cat. No. 45)

15–16. GIOVANNI LORENZO BERNINI: STUDIES FOR THE CIBORIUM IN THE CAPPELLA DEL SS. SACRAMENTO, ST. PETER'S (Cat. Nos. 30 and 28)

17. PIETRO DA CORTONA: THE TROOPS OF ALEXANDER ASSAULTING PERA   (Cat. No. 608)

18. PIETRO DA CORTONA: THE CONVERSION OF ST. PAUL (Cat. No. 614)

19. PIETRO DA CORTONA: TANCRED WOUNDED (Cat. No. 603)

20. ATTRIBUTED TO PIETRO DA CORTONA: AUGUSTUS AND THE SIBYL (Cat. No. 622)

21. PIETRO DA CORTONA: THE DEATH OF TURNUS (Cat. No. 605)

22. PIETRO DA CORTONA: SAMSON KILLING THE PHILISTINE (Cat. No. 611)

23. PIETRO DA CORTONA: A SAINT RECEIVING A PAIR OF MANACLES FROM THE VIRGIN (Cat. No. 616)

24. ANDREA SACCHI: ST. FRANCIS AND OTHER SAINTS ADORING THE VIRGIN AND CHILD (Cat. No. 768)

25. ANDREA SACCHI: TOBIAS LEAVING HIS FAMILY (Cat. No. 767)

26. ANDREA SACCHI: AN *IGNUDO* (Cat. No. 808)

27. ANDREA SACCHI: STUDY FOR A DECORATIVE SCHEME (Cat. No. 805)

28. ANDREA SACCHI: ELIJAH ASCENDING TO HEAVEN (Cat. No. 766)

29. SASSOFERRATO: THE MARRIAGE OF ST. CATHERINE (Cat. No. 879)

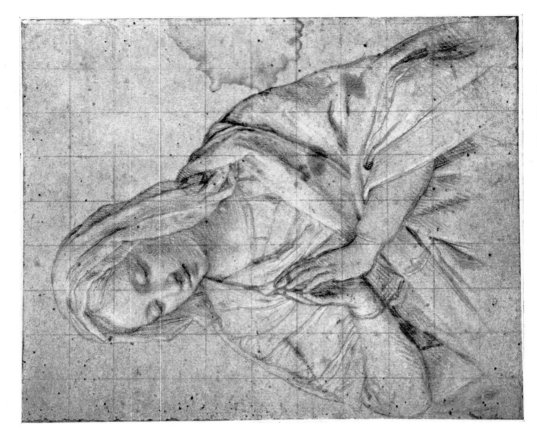

31. SASSOFERRATO: THE MADONNA (Cat No. 877)

30. SASSOFERRATO: THE MADONNA AND CHILD WITH ST. JOHN
(Cat. No. 888)

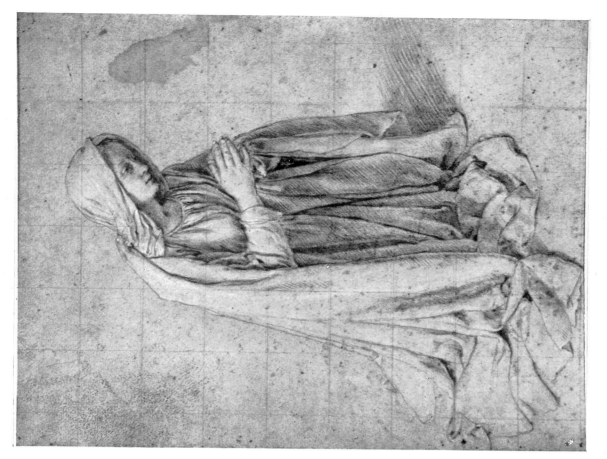

33. SASSOFERRATO: THE VIRGIN FROM THE NATIVITY (Cat. No. 882)

32. SASSOFERRATO: AN ANGEL FROM A CRUCIFIXION (Cat. No. 899)

34. SASSOFERRATO: PORTRAIT OF AN ECCLESIASTIC (Cat. No. 926)

35. SASSOFERRATO: PORTRAIT OF A CARDINAL (Cat. No. 897)

36. SASSOFERRATO: JUDITH WITH THE HEAD OF HOLOFERNES (Cat. No. 903)

37. SASSOFERRATO: ST. ANTHONY ABBOT (Cat. No. 918)

38. SASSOFERRATO: HEAD OF A CARDINAL (Cat. No. 929)

39. SASSOFERRATO: HEAD OF A MAN WITH LONG HAIR (Cat. No. 931)

40. PIER FRANCESCO MOLA: LANDSCAPE WITH FIGURES BESIDE A STREAM (Cat. No. 546)

41. PIER FRANCESCO MOLA: VENUS FINDING THE DEAD ADONIS (Cat. No. 541)

42. PIER FRANCESCO MOLA: THE HOLY FAMILY (Cat. No. 539)

43. CIRO FERRI: MOSES STRIKING THE ROCK (Cat. No. 125)

44. JACQUES COURTOIS: A BATTLE (Cat. No. 117)

45. GIOVANNI PAOLO SCHOR: DESIGN FOR THE BACK OF A COACH WITH A VICTORIOUS WARRIOR
(Cat. No. 952)

46. GIOVANNI PAOLO SCHOR: DESIGN FOR THE BACK OF A COACH WITH FIGURES OF FAITH, FORTITUDE
AND TRUTH (Cat. No. 951)

47. LUIGI GARZI: ST. CATHERINE RECEIVED INTO HEAVEN
(Cat. No. 137)

48. GIOVANNI BATTISTA GAULLI: ALLEGORY OF JUSTICE
(Cat. No. 146)

49. GIOVANNI BATTISTA GAULLI: THE SACRIFICE OF NOAH (Cat. No. 149)

50. GIOVANNI BATTISTA GAULLI: VENUS AND ADONIS (Cat. No. 155)

51. CARLO MARATTA: ALLEGORY IN HONOUR OF AN UNKNOWN ROMAN GENTLEMAN (Cat. No. 317)

52. CARLO MARATTA: THE VIRGIN AND CHILD ADORED BY ST. MICHAEL AND OTHER SAINTS
(Cat. No. 323)

53. CARLO MARATTA: THE IMMACULATA WITH ST. GREGORY, ST. CHRYSOSTOM,
ST. JOHN AND ST. AUGUSTINE (Cat. No. 286)

54. CARLO MARATTA: THE MADONNA WITH ST. FRANCIS AND ST. JAMES (Cat. No. 283)

55. CARLO MARATTA: THE MADONNA WITH ST. FRANCIS AND ST. JAMES (Cat. No. 284)

56. CARLO MARATTA: HEAD OF ST. JOSEPH (Cat. No. 278)

57. CARLO MARATTA: HEAD OF HOLOFERNES (Cat. No. 288)

58. CARLO MARATTA: ST. CHARLES BORROMEO (Cat. No. 287)

59. CARLO MARATTA: STUDY FOR THE MARTYRDOM OF ST. BLAISE AND ST. SEBASTIAN
(Cat. No. 265)

60. CARLO MARATTA: CARDINAL ANTONIO BARBERINI (Cat. No. 300)

61. CARLO MARATTA: FRA BONAVENTURA OF BARCELONA (Cat. No. 320)

62. GIUSEPPE PASSERI: THE TRIUMPH OF ST. THOMAS AQUINAS (Cat. No. 582)

63. GIUSEPPE PASSERI: A BATTLE OUTSIDE A WALLED TOWN (Cat. No. 585)

64. ATTRIBUTED TO POMPEO BATONI: AN ALLEGORY OF MUSIC (Cat. No. 11)

65. FRANCESCO TREVISANI: THE HOLY FAMILY (Cat. No. 1000)

66. CAMILLO RUSCONI: SAINT MATTHEW (Cat. No. 737)

CONCORDANCE

CONCORDANCE

Windsor Inventory No.	Blunt Catalogue No.	Windsor Inventory No.	Blunt Catalogue No.	Windsor Inventory No.	Blunt Catalogue No.	Windsor Inventory No.	Blunt Catalogue No.	Windsor Inventory No.	Blunt Catalogue No.
053	705	354	1074	4118	296	4181	306	4245	403
055	851	513	1075	4119	367	4182	291	4246	428
097	176	882	869	4120	353	4183	289	4247	405
0118	1060	883	1065	4121	340	4184	292	4248	406
0142	723	1327	1024	4122	274	4185	290	4249	407
0150	727	1332	12	4123	273	4186	438	4250	408
0151	726	1504	548	4124	297	4187	481	4251	404
0152	728	1550	78	4125	298	4188	489	4252	393
0154	730	1768	521	4126	264	4189	508	4253	394
0155	735	1776	1040	4127	335	4190	490	4254	395
0156	736	1803	141	4128	263	4191	510	4255	396
0175	118	1940	236	4129	333	4192	515	4256	397
0176	1034	2029	1080	4130	276	4193	491	4257	443
0177	113	2045	240	4131	370	4194	304	4258	398
0179	119	2050	235	4132	287	4195	285	4259	399
0183	766	2063	1067	4133v	303	4196	473	4260	400
0197	109	2068	233	4134	15	4197	488	4261	471
0198	1020	2102	191	4135	256	4198	517	4262	414
0199	1019	2103	204	4136	275	4199	309	4263	425
0209	537	2340	1005	4137	255	4200	509	4264	426
0245	112	3369	866	4138	316	4201	419	4265	409
0251	63	3462	238	4139	371	4202	310	4266	413
0254	1003	3538	554	4140	346	4203	338	4267	468
0257	535	3539	553	4141	347	4204	507	4268	469
0258	158	3542	99	4142	305	4205	482	4269	392
0259	1028	3543	102	4143	337	4206	783	4270	514
0261	575	3547	722	4144	267	4207	502	4271	492
0262	579	3580	242	4145	1041	4208	486	4272	475
0263	572	3598	541	4146	324	4209	487	4273	474
0264	583	3606	1054	4147	326	4210	437	4274	476
0265	577	3608	743	4148	163	4211	281	4275	478
0266	585	3748	660	4149	302	4212	483	4276	477
0267	586	3753	1002	4150	283	4213	363	4277	493
0268	581	3809	707	4151	266	4214	442	4278	512
0269	576	3810	1001	4152	92	4215	445	4279	775
0270	568	4090	506	4153	496	4216	343	4280	776
0271	580	4091	317	4154	272	4217	280	4281	472
0272	569	4092	318	4155	332	4218	356	4292	436
0273	584	4093	269	4156	1052	4219	354	4296	446
0274	570	4094	768	4157	1061	4220	518	4297	447
0275	578	4095	767	4158	504	4221	314	4298	448
0276	573	4096	286	4159	268	4223	282	4299	454
0277	574	4097	323	4160	365	4224	503	4300	462
0278	571	4098	13	4161	295	4225	516	4301	457
0299	1079	4099	311	4162	300	4226	494	4302	458
0363	1046	4100	259	4163	279	4227	257	4303	452
0468	858	4101	284	4164	277	4228	366	4304	449
0830	546	4102	330	4165	278	4229	429	4305	450
0831	544	4103	293	4166	288	4230	430	4306	463
01115	129	4104	321	4167	522	4231	431	4307	455
01117	125	4105	299	4168	737	4232	432	4308	456
01120	315	4106	360	4169	261	4233	420	4309	459
01121	608	4107	361	4170	265	4234	421	4310	460
01123	14	4108	388	4171	348	4235	422	4311	461
01197	711	4109	369	4172	742	4236	423	4312	451
01198	1018	4110	359	4173	258	4237	417	4313	453
01216	96	4111	342	4174	334	4238	418	4314	427
01217	97	4112	389	4175	770	4239	410	4315	415
01219	721	4113	336	4176	527	4240	411	4316	435
01228	103	4114	357	4177	186	4241	412	4317	433
01229	104	4115	364	4178	680	4242	440	4318	434
01231	567	4116	362	4179	167	4243	401	4319	424
298	513	4117	374	4180	312	4244	402	4321	464

Windsor Inventory No.	Blunt Catalogue No.	Windsor Inventory No.	Blunt Catalogue No.	Windsor Inventory No.	Blunt Catalogue No.	Windsor Inventory No.	Blunt Catalogue No.	Windsor Inventory No.	Blunt Catalogue No.
4322	511	4405	696	4479	663	4859	852	4933	811
4323	439	4406	677	4480	970	4860	751	4934	763
4324	416	4407	501	4481	602	4861	804	4935	820
4325	444	4408	678	4482	657	4862	747	4936	848
4327	470	4409a	671	4483	616	4863	746	4937	809
4328	480	4409b	672	4484	613	4864	771	4938	797
4329	479	4410	682	4485	610	4865	772	4939	802
4330	322	4411	692	4486	1053	4866	781	4940	753
4331	465	4412	668	4487	126	4867	760	4941	805
4332	466	4413	669	4488	656	4868	868	4942	773
4333	467	4414	710	4489	1050	4869	745	4943	759
4338	349	4415	708	4492	147	4870	807	4944	774
4339	350	4416	531	4493	651	4871	806	4945	817
4340	351	4417	709	4495	597	4872	741	4946	800
4341	352	4418	1023	4499	654	4873	1006	4947	812
4342	345	4419	685	4501	133	4874	1077	4948	855a
4344	1022	4420	1044	4502	566	4875	762	4949	782
4345	769	4421	86	4503	615	4876	867	4950	793
4346	59	4422	1084	4504	603	4877b	778	4951	819
4347	761	4423	85	4506	131	4878	779	4952	813
4349	740	4424	935	4507	130	4879	358	4953	814
4350	184	4425	679	4508	609	4880	497	4954	849
4351	93	4426	520	4509	594	4881	865	4955	748
4352	135	4427	536	4510	614	4882	855	4956	850
4353	270	4428	716	4511	732	4884	810	4957	803
4354	325	4429	673	4512	731	4885	780	4958	755
4355	341	4430	675	4513	937	4886	749	4959	752
4356	327	4431	691	4514	607	4887	738	4960	95
4357	329	4432	676	4515	588	4888	824	4961	1064
4358	339	4433	684	4516	91	4889	825	4962	791
4359	307	4434	598	4517	622	4890	826	4963	796
4360	271	4435	294	4518	124	4891	827	4964	801
4361	519	4436	693	4519	604	4892	828	4965	816
4362	525	4437	623	4521	725	4893	829	4966	798
4363	355	4438	624	4522	729	4894	830	4967	790
4364r	308	4439	625	4523	117	4895	831	4968	808
4364v	313	4440	626	4524	605	4896	832	4969	799
4366	320	4441	949	4525	160	4897	833	4970	784
4367	344	4442	946	4526	606	4898	864	4971	789
4368	331	4443	940	4527	1021	4899	834	4972	786
4369	1066	4444	942	4528	618	4900	862	5055	1017
4371	387	4445	941	4529	619	4901	835	5141	106
4372	377	4446	589	4530	620	4902	98	5148	498
4373	375	4447	639	4531	590	4903	836	5170	368
4374	376	4448	591	4532	132	4904	837	5176	558
4377	378	4449	592	4533	595	4905	857	5177	559
4378	382	4450	638	4534	134	4906	792	5184	252
4379	384	4451	593	4535	1009	4907	838	5185	253
4380	373	4452	601	4536	1008	4908	1069	5186	528
4381	386	4453	666	4537	244	4909	94	5188	1073
4382	380	4454	965	4538	243	4911	71	5203	853
4383	379	4455	964	4539	178	4912	1070	5204	582
4384	381	4456	599	4540	611	4913	839	5310	1058
4385	441	4457	947	4542	939	4914	861	5311	1059
4386	383	4458	961	4543	938	4915	840	5312	662
4387	385	4459	627	4544	246	4916	841	5316	1004
4388	390	4460	972	4545	247	4917	842	5329	1000
4389	391	4461	952	4546	248	4918	843	5347	230
4390	5a	4462	951	4547	249	4919	844	5360	177
4391	777	4463	953	4583	1030	4920	845	5361	1078
4392	319	4464	966	4847	854	4921	750	5370	10
4393	484	4465	968	4848	821	4922	795	5375	6
4394	372	4467	977	4849	859	4923	756	5376	108
4396	701	4468	976	4850	860	4924	818	5377	547
4397	702	4469	948	4851	822	4925	815	5380	529
4398	697	4470	975	4852	823	4926	754	5392	499
4399	698	4471	1011	4853	105	4927	794	5393	530
4400	700	4472	617	4854	788	4928	846	5405	1076
4401	699	4473	659	4855	787	4929	847	5512	856
4402	703	4474	658	4856	744	4930	757	5516	169
4403	534	4475	301	4857	765	4931	764	5517	1045
4404	533	4478	653	4858	739	4932	758	5520	1063

Windsor Inventory No.	Blunt Catalogue No.	Windsor Inventory No.	Blunt Catalogue No.	Windsor Inventory No.	Blunt Catalogue No.	Windsor Inventory No.	Blunt Catalogue No.	Windsor Inventory No.	Blunt Catalogue No.
5526	1082	5607	73	5686	197	6053	877	6349	115
5529	72	5608	1010	5687	193	6054	880	6350	1007
5530	56	5609	22	5688	198	6055	896	6705	175
5531	156	5610	67	5689	227	6056	906	6706	173
5532	46	5611	68	5690	225	6057	911	6707	172
5533	157	5612	49	5691	234	6058	874	6708	170
5534	863	5613	48	5692	212	6059	875	6709	171
5535	652	5614	26	5693	199	6060	901	6713	1047
5536	1072	5615	18	5694	200	6061	915	6714	179
5537	60	5616	162	5695	224	6063	887	6715	180
5538	621	5617	50	5696	209	6064	895	6716	181
5539	54	5618	51	5697	190	6065	882	6717	1048
5540	53	5619	954	5698	207	6066	883	6718	1033
5541	58	5620	967	5700	216	6067	886	6719	139
5542	57	5621	39	5701	211	6068	921	6721	4
5543	55	5623	41	5702	201	6069	918	6723	90
5544	152	5624	44	5703	215	6070	900	6724	89
5545	151	5625	40	5704	185	6071	909	6725	88
5546	183	5626	38	5705	219	6072	899	6726	87
5547	149	5627	45	5706	206	6073	881	6727	720
5548	153	5628	37	5707	223	6074	891	6728	9
5549	166	5629	1012	5708	226	6075	907	6730	719
5550	146	5630	1013	5709	187	6076	923	6731	7
5551	871	5631	1014	5710	222	6077	922	6732	8
5552	140	5632	1015	5711	205	6078	903	6733	11
5553	262	5633	1016	5712	1068	6079	916	6734	713
5554	150	5634	66	5713	239	6080	892	6735	712
5555	1057	5635	23	5716	208	6081	913	6736	714
5556	974	5636	24	5717	188	6082	885	6737	1038
5557	70	5637	25	5718	210	6083	912	6738	870
5558	34	5642	973	5719	217	6084	879	6742	1035
5559	52	5643	956	5721	213	6085	908	6745	734
5560	28	5644	524	5728	557	6086	919	6746	168
5561	29	5645	715	5755	1083	6087	889	6749	1036
5562	30	5646	717	5805	550	6088	890	6750	1031
5563	161	5647	526	5816	1081	6089	920	6751	1037
5564	27	5648	694	5821	100	6090	917	6753	136
5565	43	5649	670	5822	101	6091	914	6755	1056
5566	16	5650	718	5931	987	6092	904	6758	81
5567	960	5651	500	5932	983	6093	898	6761	155
5568	165	5652	680a	5933	980	6094	905	6763	706
5569	79	5653	674	5934	985	6095	888	6764	2
5570	17	5654	1039	5935	986	6096	260	6765	1085
5571	75	5655	688	5936	984	6097	328	6766	542
5572	978	5656	683	5937	982	6098	936	6769a	645
5573	963	5657	689	5938	979	6099	934	6769b	646
5574	971	5658	695	5939	981	6100	926	6770a	641
5575	959	5659	690	5940	996	6101	928	6770b	642
5576	77	5660	687a	5941	998	6102	897	6771	643
5577	76	5661	667	5942	988	6103	924	6772	644
5578	962	5662	681	5943	997	6104	925	6773	647
5579	958	5663	686	5944	993	6105	894	6774a	648
5580	957	5664	687	5945	989	6106	927	6774b	649
5581	969	5665	704	5946	995	6107	933	6775	523
5582	955	5666	241	5947	990	6108	930	6776	539
5584	65	5667	218	5948	991	6109	931	6778	1
5585	64	5668	220	5949	994	6110	932	6783	114
5586	47	5669	232	5950	992	6111	929	6785	549
5587	69	5670	196	5951	999	6112	873	6789	154
5588	19	5671	142	5952	3	6115	237	6790	82
5589	36	5672	1029	5953	5	6120	1062	6791	1042
5592	950	5674	194	5954	1032	6123	116	6792	1055
5596	32	5675	189	5983	1030a	6135	552	6793	174
5598	945	5676	231	5986	733	6136	551	6795	111
5599	20	5678	228	5998	121	6151	545	6796	84
5600	148	5679	214	6046	910	6154	254	6798	540
5601	80	5680	195	6047	878	6159	556	6799	538
5602	33	5681	203	6048	902	6161	555	6802	600
5603	35	5682	229	6049	884	6162	543	6804	1025
5604	21	5683	192	6050	876	6336	120	6805	1027
5605	62	5684	202	6051	505	6345	123	6806	587
5606	61	5685	221	6052	893	6348	122	6807	650

Windsor Inventory No.	Blunt Catalogue No.	Windsor Inventory No.	Blunt Catalogue No.	Windsor Inventory No.	Blunt Catalogue No.	Windsor Inventory No.	Blunt Catalogue No.
6808	182	6824	137	7707	532	10772	564
6810	251	6825	138	8322	1051	10773	565
6811	1049	6826	143	8373	631	10893	785
6812	145	6827	144	8648	630	10911	640
6813	1043	6831	664	8718	629	11152	633
6814	250	6832	596	8805	632	11592	31
6815	872	6833	245	10382	634	11593	74
6816	665	6834	612	10383	635	11594	943
6817	110	6835	127	10384	636	11595	944
6818	1026	6836	128	10748	628	12064	637
6819	83	6338	495	10758	42	12070	724
6820	661	6839	655	10770	562	13038	1071
6821	107	7706	561	10771	563	13107	560
6822	159						

Schor: The Arms of Pope Clement X (Cat. No. 949)

INDEX OF SUBJECTS

St. Gregory, The Mass of, 765
St. Hubert, 219
St. James, 261, 285
St. James, St. Martin and the Beggar, and a Bishop, 121
St. Jerome, 327, 524, 1006
St. John the Baptist, 542, 680a, 901, 1029
St. John on Patmos, 3
St. Joseph, 277–9, 304, 911, 916
St. Lawrence, 85, 246–9, 921
St. Louis, 115–6, 266, 690–1
St. Luke, 191, 266
St. Margaret, 326, 922
St. Mark, 175, 190
St. Martin and the beggar, St. James, and a Bishop, 121
St. Matthew, 194, 737
St. Paul, 2, 126, 130, 168, 233, 614–5
St. Peter, 6, 130, 168, 203, 309–10, 1009
St. Philip Neri, 262, 302–3, 686–7a
St. Sebastian, 4, 264, 1030
St. Simon, Martyrdom of, 196
St. Stanislas Kotska, Vision of, 272
St. Stephen receiving St. Bernard into Cîteaux, 567
St. Theresa receiving the Carmelite Order from the Virgin, 215
St. Thomas, 199
St. Thomas Aquinas, 582, 764
Saints (unidentified), 5, 124, 232, 616, 708–10, 980, 1034, 1037–8, 1041
Samson killing the Philistine, 611
Solomon, 173–4, 725
Tobias leaving his Family, 305, 767
Triumph of the Church, 64
Virgin:
　　Assumption of, 91, 184, 572, 685–87a
　　Birth of, 256, 673
　　Coronation of, 84, 1023
　　Immaculate Conception of, 147, 286, 712, 881
　　Presentation in the Temple of, 672
　　Visitation of, 1018
　　See also: Madonna

CLASSICAL SUBJECTS

Alexander assaulting Pera, 608
Alexander, Victory over Porus, 637
Apelles painting Campaspe, 694
Apollo, 94–5, 936
Apollo and Minerva on Parnassus, 1051
Apollo Belvedere, 373–4
Apollo crowning the Singer Pasquali, 495
Augustus and the Sibyl, 622
Aurora, 741–2
Bacchanal, 982
Bacchus, 382, 588, 737
Bacchus and Ariadne, 538
Caelus, Founder of Praeneste, 600

Camillus and the Schoolmaster of Falerii, 727
Ceres, 867
Charity, 1056–7
Claudia, Vestal Virgin, 134
Coriolanus, 728
Darius before Alexander, 180
Diana, 314, 736
Diana and Endymion, 1052
Flora, 378–9
Flora, Ceres, Bacchus and Vertumnus, 735
Foundation of Rome, Allegory of, 770
Hercules, 380–1
Hercules and Antaeus, 984
Homer, 389
Juno and Aeolus, 606
La Tintura della Rosa, 257–9
Lucius Verus, 385
Lucretia stabbing herself, 340
Maenad, 386
Marcus Aurelius, 375–6, 383
Marcus Curius Dentatus, 182
Mars and Venus discovered by Vulcan, 695
Mercury ordering Aeneas to leave Carthage, 183
Midas, Feast of, 983
Minerva, 338, 718, 1051
Muse, 384
Mutius Scaevola, 139–40, 731
Nova Nupta, 387
Nymph, Centaurs and a Leopard, 855a
Pasquali crowned by Apollo, 495
Perseus being armed by Jupiter and Minerva, 127–8
Polyphemus hurling a rock at Ulysses, 985
Roman Soldier, 720
Romulus and Remus, 179, 662, 1054
Sabines, Rape of the, 663
Sabine women intervening between the Romans and the Sabines, 711
Sacrifices, 377, 665, 1053
Sacrifice of Iphigenia, 660, 729
Satyrs, 1055, 1058–9, 1082
Scipio, Continence of, 181
Sibyl, 341
Trajan, Justice of, 664
Tullia driving her chariot over the body of her Father, 607
Turnus, Death of, 605, 726
Venus, Head of, 388
Venus and Adonis, 155, 541
Venus and Cupid, 597
Venus and Cupid before Jupiter, 661
Venus, Cupid and Vulcan, 339

MISCELLANEOUS SUBJECTS

Alexander VII, Portrait of, 46

Allegorical Figures, 154, 160, 162, 315, 430, 508–9, 992–98, 1043
Allegory in Honour of Roman Gentleman, 317–8
Altars, Designs of, 18, 20, 28–32, 74, 129, 148, 617, 657, 784–5, 945, 974
Architectural Designs, 19, 23–7, 36, 593, 627–31, 634–6, 786, 943–4, 950, 960
Arms of Alexander VII, 66, 964
Arms of an Ecclesiastic, 1085
Arms of Don Taddeo Barberini, 602
Arms of Clement X, 949
Arms of Cardinal Lodovico Ludovisi, 769
Arms of the Barberini Family, 787–8, 953
Arms of the Chigi Family, 953
Arms of the Colonna Family, 950
Army marching out of a walled Town, 586
Arts, Allegory of the, 1049
Barberini, Cardinal Antonio, Portrait of, 300
Battle Scenes, 117, 585, 854
Bernini, Giovanni Lorenzo, Portraits of, 53–5
Canopy, Design for a, 978
Chariot, Designs for, 50–1, 951–4, 966–70
Catafalque of Carlo Barberini, Designs for, 48–9
Clement VIII in Bologna, 1030a
Clement IX, Portrait of, 342
Clement X, Portrait of, 157
Clement XI, Allegory in honour of, 693
Constantine addressing his Army, 435
Dance in Casa Falconieri, 771
Dawn, Allegory of, 1050
Decorative Designs, 16–7, 43, 161, 200–2, 245, 589, 591, 594, 599, 601, 639–40, 666, 783, 787–819, 940–2, 958–62
Drawing, Allegory of, 316
Duilius, Portrait of, 152
Eagle flying towards the Sun, 963
Erminia and the Shepherds, 135, 584
Ferdinand, King of Hungary, Allegory in Honour of, 107
Fountains, 38–45, 975–7
Frames, Designs for, 617, 787–8, 956–7, 961, 1084
Ghezzi, Giuseppe, Portrait of, 176
Giordano, Vitale, Portrait of, 151
Godfrey de Bouillon, Victory of, 1060
Hero crowned by Victory, 583
Hero, Departure of a, 730
Horsemen, 118–20, 122–3
Imperial Standard, 633
Innocence, Allegory of, 1042
Innocent XI, Portrait of, 156